Turning
the Tide

DAVID BELLAMY AND BRENDAN QUAYLE

Turning the Tide

Exploring the Options for Life on Earth

Collins

Grafton Street, London

William Collins Sons & Co. Ltd.
London · Glasgow · Sydney · Auckland · Toronto · Johannesburg

First published in Great Britain 1986
© Brendan Quayle & David Bellamy 1986

ISBN 0 00 219368 X

Typeset by Ace Filmsetting Ltd, Frome, Somerset
Colour and black-and-white origination by Adroit Photo Litho Ltd, Birmingham
Printed and bound by Wm Collins Sons & Co. Ltd, Glasgow

CONTENTS

FOR MARIANNE AND REBECCA,

HANNAH AND EOGHAIN,

AND THE CHILDREN OF THE FUTURE.

ACKNOWLEDGEMENTS

The authors would like to thank the following for their help in preparing *Turning The Tide*.

First and foremost, we owe a special debt to Gilly McWilliam, our editor at Collins and to George Courtice, series producer at Tyne Tees television.

We must thank Peter Seggar of Organic Farmers and Growers; Dr Bill Williamson and Dr Laksman Guruswami of Durham University; Peter Smith of Cleveland Co-operative Development Agency; Ian Breech and Roy Deane of Tyne Tees Television; Ray Beals and Terry Lacey of Co-operation for Development Ltd; and Francesca Dow of Collins. We are also indebted to Dr Brian Roberts; Durham Rural Community Council; Bernadette Prat of Oxfam UK; the Economic and Social Research Council of the UK; to the science and environment writers of *New Scientist*, the *Guardian* and the *Observer*; to David Dixon and the people of Botton Village.

The information in *Turning The Tide* is gleaned from a wide variety of responsible primary and secondary sources. As *Turning The Tide* is for the general reader it would not have been appropriate to have annotated the text with copious reference to sources. But every effort has been made to check on the accuracy of the material given and where there was uncertainty to consult with people and experts directly involved in the relevant fields.

Special thanks to Carol Brown, who copiously typed and retyped many versions of the original manuscript, and to Carole Reeves who did the index and generally helped out.

We owe a special debt to the production team of Tyne Tees Television, who took up the initiative for an environmental series, shared our ideas and turned them into visual and political reality, and to the film and editing crew who painstakingly transferred these ideas into film and sound. Those involved were: George Courtice (producer), Paul Dickin (director), Roy Deane (associate producer), Charlotte Stewart (researcher), Howard Beebe (film editor), Dave Dixon (lighting cameraman), Richard Edwards (assistant cameraman), Bob Rhodes (sound recordist), Jill Forbes (production assistant), Alan Sharp (electrician), Terry Pate (grips driver) and Angela Spinks (Secretary). The *Turning The Tide* series is a good example of what a local company, local talents and local minds can do, globally.

PROLOGUE
SETTING OUT

The sun rises on a new day aboard the good *Spaceship Earth*. Today, like every day since the first morning of the world, creatures stir from sleep and go about their daily routines, routines that invariably involve an element of planning ahead – the next meal, the next hunt, the next event, preparation for the next season.

But some of us are preparing for a trip which is all about planning ahead, not just for the new days which lie immediately before us, but for a more distant future. You have just joined us on that trip, a high-speed environmental journey across space and time to the very limits of our evolutionary existences. On route we shall be taking in some of the sights and sounds of the great planetary life-support systems, our water, food, fuel and genetic resources.

Our journey is a mission in two interwoven parts. We identify some of the processes which are putting the health and survival of these systems at risk, which are plundering and destroying the finite natural resources on which all life ultimately depends. But we also explore some of the options and ideas which offer an alternative to the negative technologies and policies of plunder and pollution. And it is these alternative routes and new ways which we believe provide us with the resources to go forward with renewed optimism and hope.

It's now over one billion years since an ancient tide carried onshore the primitive life-forms which were the genetic forebears of our upright evolutionary predecessors. At least another 999.9 million years were to elapse before our more recent ancestors gazed inquisitively out to sea, and began to question what lay beyond the life-bringing turning of the tide. That they were there at all was proof that they had learned how to make good use of the natural resources of environment, earth, sea and air, to sustain their own growth and development. In that respect they were just like all the other animals around them. But in other respects they had evolved differently. They had developed culture, a complex system of language, art and symbols, which set them apart from the natural world. This system served as a tool of communication by which they could build up and exchange knowledge and ideas about themselves and the world about them and pass that information across the generations. Culture thus became an additional means of ensuring the survival of the species.

In time culture diversified into the myriad different forms and patterns we know today. But our ancestors who walked on that beach had something which is not so commonly found today – a built-in reverence for the natural environment, for the forces and the resources of nature. They coloured the world about them with the names of divinities which personified and made intelligible the otherwise inexplicable powers and mysteries of existence. And in their homage to the gods and spirits of the sun, the moon, the sea, the earth, the plants, the animals and the seasons, there was contained an

understanding of the delicate and divine balance of nature, a cosmic calm which humanity could never be allowed to challenge if it wished to survive in nature. Indeed, in order to ensure a well-regulated social order, as well as food on the table, fuel in the hearth, game in the forest and water on the land, our ancestors had devised a particular series of codes, customs, rules and conventions which served to maintain that delicate and intricate balance.

But many thousands of years later, we find that balance disturbed. The critical understanding of humanity's place in nature has been usurped by a belief in unlimited growth, in unbound progress, in limitless technological achievement. And the advances that have been made to date are wholly dependent upon the ongoing, relentless conquest of nature and the endless exploitation of the world's limited natural resources. Progress has been accompanied by a veritable tide of destruction of natural systems, and has placed over our own heads the omnipresent threat of extinction. Overpopulation, the spread of nuclear technology, the stock-piling of nuclear weapons, the pollution of earth, sea and sky and the over-exploitation of our natural resources, all cast a long shadow over our future and the other living systems with which we share our journey through time on *Spaceship Earth*. It is time to turn the tide of destruction.

And there is hope for the future, a hope contained in a renewed understanding of the balance of nature and the limits to growth, and in the pursuit by some of new processes, technologies and practices which are sensitive to the environment. But there can be no hope without action; without the taking of positive decisions to turn that tide of destruction; without the formulation of new guidelines for the forward march of human progress. There can be no hope without the adoption of ethics for a new era of environmental concern and understanding.

Our environmental journey charts some of these ethics and guidelines. We shine a light on the good decisions that have and are being made, and on the people who are making them, who are showing the way forward with action, insight, argument and good example. The light reflected back is radiantly green, growing daily in strength and power, and fuelled by a determination and optimism against which our old entrenched ideas and ways appear colourless and stale.

We are all travellers on *Spaceship Earth*, and the outcome of what we see on our environmental journey concerns us all. At the moment, the support systems of our planet, despite their considerable capacities for self-renewal, are in a precarious condition. The operators currently sitting at the helm haven't the faintest idea where we're going. Our vital life-support systems are right out of their control, and we seem to be plunging forward deeper and deeper into a dark abyss – *Spaceship Earth*'s final twilight. Fortunately, a new breed of controllers with a clearer view of the way ahead, are struggling to take the helm and lead us back from the edge. Our duty, the responsibility of us all, is to give them that chance.

'... man learned to make good use of the natural resources of earth, sea and air ...'

On our new day the sun is now full up, and it's all systems go for our environmental journey across space and time. On land, the air is warm and bright, a good omen for what lies ahead. Out at sea the tide is right out, but change is in the air.

1 COMING DOWN TO EARTH

AROUND THE WORLD AND BACK AGAIN

The first destination on our environmental journey is the north-east of England, land of coalmines and shipyards, of dramatic coastlines and the great rolling moors and dales of the Cheviots and the North Pennines. These are uplifting, living environments, with a rich culture and a deep character. But parts of them are under threat from decline and dereliction, and these same threats, in varying forms and intensities, occur right across the globe. And we see history repeating itself. What is happening today, in quiet upland English villages, in the tropical rainforests of South America, in the industrial conurbations of the First World, is similar to what happened to the North American Indian over two hundred years ago.

To find out why, we venture back through time to the lands and living rooms of thirty years ago, when the worst of our present troubles really began, when we really began to completely lose our sense of balance. We also return to the roots of the new social movements of conservation and environmentalism, and explore how they are managing to re-assert old balances.

We live in a dangerous present. But by looking into the past, and by taking a long-term, greener view of the future, we uncover some promising directions in which to go forward.

BRINGING IT ALL BACK HOME

The world's problems are all around us — they start right in our own homes — in what we eat, how we live, in everything we do. So we start our environmental journey no further away than David Bellamy's local fish and chip shop in the north-east of England . . .

It was some thirty years ago. In the days when fish and chips were still served wrapped up in newsprint. As the old lady behind the counter handed over his hot, high-calorie package, a picture of a starving child in Africa caught her eye. *'Strange'* she said, *'that two thirds of the world are starving while the other third is slimming.'*

David had no ready response, but it brought home to him that even the most basic of our actions — like buying that portion of fish and chips — had world-wide implications. He had been suddenly catapulted from a local action into global thinking.

Thirty years on that same chip shop is still there. But the old lady has gone . . . and the world outside has changed out of all proportion. Starvation is still around though – despite all the progress we've made on so many fronts inside those thirty years. Dying from lack of food or from diseases brought on by malnutrition is a daily reality in many parts of the globe, a fact of life as basic and familiar as a bag of chips is to us.

The harvests of the world, the fresh bounty of land and sea, are shared out between humankind in a very unfair way. And that's not the only imbalance. One third of the world also consumes most of the other raw materials of daily life. The world's ores, metals, fibres, its primary sources of energy, its stocks of coal, oil and gas are used up at a terrifying rate to keep us in the style to which we have grown accustomed – at the expense of the rest of humanity and of our planet earth. Starvation, resource depletion, pollution, arms proliferation . . . it's all part and parcel of a hidden, undeclared but unceasing war against the natural and human environment.

Underlying the imbalance between north and south, between First World and Third World – a global economic disorder – there is an ecological disorder. In order to keep pace with the existing demands of consumption in the First World and the rising demands and needs of the Third World, we are depleting our natural resources of soil, energy and genetic stock at a relentless pace. And with the waste-products of our industrial and chemical processes we are polluting our seas, rivers and skies.

Yet despite our rapid consumption of resources, tens of millions of people die of starvation or related diseases every year, and another 800 million subsist on the edge of absolute poverty, confined to a miserable existence on the margins of 'civilization'. As they struggle to survive, the forests fall and the deserts spread. Development programmes initiated to relieve poverty tend to intensify it, leaving poor countries struggling to pay off enormous debts to rich countries.

In many places, disaffection with the current order of things leads to revolt, unrest, riot and terrorism. And the entrenched powers that be compete for control of dwindling resources and a dwindling share in a contracting market. These are the countries rich in technological prowess, that trade widely in armaments abroad in order to finance their development and stock-piling at home.

The sense of affinity with place, of being part of the environment – are lost when traditional communities are uprooted and drift to cramped living on city margins. Above Desolate high-rise blocks in the UK. Below A shanty town in Haiti.

This may all seem a far cry from a bag of chips in northern England. But these days, even if you go on a sight-seeing tour or a quiet ramble across the top of the moors, the prospect of cataclysm can bring you back to reality with a nasty jolt. Missile-carrying jet fighters scream through the valleys below, rehearsing bombing runs for a third world war, while in the distance, artillery shells pound the boggy tracts of a military testing ground. If you look around as you go about your everyday life, you can see more signs of the global environmental crisis. From our launching pad in the North Pennines, we can see how this area has suffered from the imbalance within and between the economic and ecological systems of the late 20th century. Like much of north-east England, the Pennines have been experiencing a gradual recession over the last thirty years, which has meant lost

*Abandoned lead mine
workshops in the northern
Pennines – the watery grave of
a once-thriving community.*

jobs, declining services, an ageing population, a declining environment, and
dying villages.

An elderly villager of Allenheads, one of the highest inhabited places in
England, talked of the decline that was eating away the heart of the community in
which she lived. She remembered the warmth, work and promise of earlier days.

> 'When we came there was a host of estate workers, there wasn't a wall down or a
> stone out of place; now, there are no workers at all. When the mines were
> going, it used to be a clang and clatter in that yard the whole time; now, it's all
> silent. Allenheads is a village of pensioners, a dying village; there's no work . . .
> soon there'll be nothing left.'

Allenheads is not alone. Similar stories of economic decline and environmental
dereliction can be found across the length and breadth of Britain's uplands, the
last of the country's great wilderness areas. The chief cause of the problem in
Allenheads and the rest of the North Pennines is a combination of neglect,
misuse, and lack of investment. In other upland areas of Britain, there are other
pressures too: over-intensive tourism causing ecological damage in the Lake
District and the Peak District; landscape acidification; over-intensive afforestation and agricultural exploitation in the North York Moors. The common factor
is an imbalance between the economic uses to which we put the hills, and the
well-being of the ecological systems which make them special. They are sensitive
environments. Soils are thin and subject to high winds, heavy annual rain and
snowfall. The predations of man, over-cropping the vegetation, draining the

damp fell, exposing the soil through ploughing, burning the heather, planting acid-loving conifers, tramping across hill-sides, blasting the rocks for minerals, take an unbearably heavy toll on the ecological health of the hills.

The economic health is also undermined. Today's insistence upon maximum production of sheep, grouse, stone and trees now, means resource depletion, less production, less output in the future. And it's this policy of 'taking out while the going is good' in the recent past that set in train the problems of decline and dereliction. The social and economic fabric of some 30% of Britain's most beautiful and inspiring landscape is at risk. There is nothing natural or inevitable about the problems of Britain's uplands. They are a direct result of how we interact with nature and the natural world. The social and environmental problems which we create for ourselves and for the generations which follow are a direct result of bad management and lack of foresight. The voice of Allenheads – of a changing, threatened environment – can be found throughout the passages of history and throughout the world. The circumstances vary, the causes change, but whether the First or Third World, the message is invariably the same: dislocation, disruption, destruction, stagnation, decline and decay.

Traditional rural societies, living at first hand with nature, are always at the sharp end of environmental and resource mis-management. Attacks on their environment are, in effect, attacks on their culture, livelihoods and lives. Perhaps the most tragic case of this in history is that of the American Indian. The Indians possessed a remarkable appreciation of nature and its delicate balances – which was clearly not shared by the invaders from the east. As an old Wintu Indian recalled:

> 'When we kill meat, we eat it all up; we don't chop down the trees, we only use dead wood. But the white people plough up the ground, pull down the trees, kill everything. The spirit of the land hates them. The Indians never hurt anything, but the white people destroy all. Everywhere the white man has touched it, the earth is sore.'[1]

But the new settlers had their own ideas of how to manage nature and of how to trade and make use of its resources. For the Creek Indians in the 1790s, it meant the loss of their lands, the death of their nation ... the end of the trail. As one Creek chief said:

> 'On this land there is a great deal of timber, pine and oak, which are of much use to the white man. They send it to foreign countries, and it brings them a great deal of money. On the land there is much grass for cattle and horses, and much good food for hogs. On this land there is a great deal of tobacco raised, which likewise brings much money. Even the streams are valuable to the white man, to grind the wheat and corn that grows on this land. The pine trees which are dead are valuable for tar.
>
> 'All these things are lasting benefits. If we hold our lands, there will always be a turkey, or deer, or a fish in the streams, for those young who will come after us. We are afraid if we part with any more of our lands the white people will not suffer us to keep as much as will be sufficient to bury our dead.'[2]

Overleaf
A beautiful upland landscape in the English Peak District ... but the ruins speak of an abandoned community; the heavy afforestation of an unbalanced acid landscape; the reservoir of the destruction of acres of sensitive marginal habitat ...

Raising totems to a glorious past – from the present-day confines of an Indian reservation.

The fate of the Indian, the Plains Buffalo and the North American Wilderness is well known, a thing of the past. But over 200 years later we find the same things still happening across the globe. Possibly the worst cases of environmental destruction are in the world's great gene-rich tropical rainforests, particularly those in South America. The modern scourges of the tropical rainforest involve clearance for agricultural purposes and for big dam developments. The projects involved are largely financed with the help of massive capital injections from respectable, international development bodies like the World Bank. They are mostly the product of well-intentioned development packages, guaranteeing energy, industry and usually urban 'progress'. But the long-term injection is pure unadulterated destruction: the devastation of a dwindling tropical forest reserve, the extermination of wildlife, the impoverishment and starvation of indigenous peoples, and the saddling of the host countries with enormous debts. Huge budget deficits bring with them a permanent state of economic crisis and an unremitting cycle of social and civil disorder, often leading to guerilla warfare, bloody revolution, and constant counter-insurgency.

The headman of Guiana's Akawaio Indians, opposing one such mega-scheme, the damming of the Upper Mazaruni River, spoke of the destruction which would befall his people.

'This land is where we are at home, we know its way. It is needed for those who come after us. The spirits around us know us and are friendly and helpful. This land keeps us together within its mountains – we come to understand that we are not just a few people or separate villages, but one people belonging to a homeland. If we had to move, we would be lost to those who remain in other villages. This would be a sadness to us all, like the sadness of death.'[3]

Sometimes the pleadings turn to dismay, to anger or even violence. The Chico Dam development in the Philippines which threatened to disposses the Bontoc and Kalinga tribes-people led to the following tract, complete with graphic images of protest, being daubed on walls:

THE DAMS ARE ALL WE TALK ABOUT THESE DAYS. IT IS LIKE TALKING CONTINUALLY OF DEATH, OF CERTAIN DEATH. THE PRESIDENT WILL HAVE TO PUT US ALL IN PRISON IF HE WANTS TO CONTINUE WITH THE CONSTRUCTION OF THE DAMS ON THE CHICO. BETTER STILL, HE SHOULD BOMB US OUT OF EXISTENCE. THIS WOULD BE MUCH EASIER FOR HIM AND FOR US, BECAUSE WE ARE NOT GOING TO ALLOW THE DESTRUCTION OF OUR HOMES AND FIELDS AS LONG AS THE BREATH OF LIFE IS IN US,

But just as these voices raised in protest have their counterpart back home in England, so too do the projects which inspire the protests.[4] In the Pennines these days, damming and blasting is mostly limited to quarrying and to artillery practice on desolate moors. But not so long ago, in the 1960s there was the Cow Green Dam and Reservoir scheme in Upper Teesdale.

In the Cow Green project no lives or livelihoods were directly threatened. It was proposed to impound some of the waters of the High Pennines by building a dam in an uninhabited place. And by providing extra resources of water to feed the thirsty steel and chemical industries of Tees-side the livelihoods of others could be ensured. But the natural habitat of one of Europe's most unique and precious natural reserves was threatened ... a botanical treasure house glistening with species jewels like the Teesdale violet and the bog sandwort, the yellow mountain saxifrage and spring gentian. Flowers like these – sparkling crystal remnants of the Great Ice Age – envelope in their leaves, roots and plant genes, a millennia of ancient botanical time. An Act of Parliament had to be passed before any development could go ahead, and developers and industrialists had to contend with scientists and nature conservationists.

After months of battling and screaming headlines in the local press, the bill was passed. The struggle for conserving this particular patch of high ground was lost. A rush programme of scientific investigation and transplanting was set in motion to save the rare species of Cow Green and Widdybank Fell. The government of the day had made a value judgement. When it came down to a choice between the profits of the chemical industry of the Lower Tees, and a unique collection of rare flora, they were in no doubt as to which they thought was the most valuable. Today, Upper Teesdale has accommodated the elephantine dam at its head and the submergence of some of its rarest plant communities. The lake has an undoubted beauty of its own, a mirror to the fells reflecting the moods of the environment and the march of the seasons. Wading birds stalk the artificial shallows of the lake edge, while lapwing, curlew, redshank, dunlin, sandpiper and oystercatcher nest close to its shore. There are fish, invertebrates and plankton galore, and more human visitors with eyes curious for wildlife than ever before.

But the irreplaceable natural habitats of a wealth of gene-rich species were lost to history and future generations. And the mirror of lakewater on which the developers' hopes and costs had been so briefly reflected was shattered by an incoming tide of industrial recession. Now, in the 1980s, with industries closing down, chemical plants being moved abroad and the highest unemployment rate in the country, Tees-side's economic gain was short-lived. Many environmental battles have been fought, won and lost across the globe since Cow Green. The demand for an environmental and long-term assessment of economic choices and future needs has become greater, but the voice of fast progress and short-term development still commands the air-waves and still stalks the corridors of advice and decision-making.

However in the 1980s, another battlefront has been opened up in the North Pennines, and this time the environmental lobby has the upper hand. It's a dispute between conservationists on the one hand and farmers and developers on the other. At question is whether the North Pennines should be designated an Area of Outstanding Natural Beauty (AONB). Official designation would bring better levels of grant aid, protect the great natural features of the area, its flora, fauna and landscape attractions, and encourage development in tourism, agriculture, leisure and small business at the same time. The farmers, developers and some local authorities, however, oppose the designation because of their concern for short-term development.

Both sides made their case at a much-publicized Public Inquiry. For the first time, the need to strike a sensible balance between conservation and development was recognized, and there is a good chance that both sides will come together to plan a new, sustainable policy for the future. Designation would undoubtedly bring national recognition and new investment for the North Pennines, creating new jobs in leisure and tourism, small businesses, and new farm enterprises. The landscape and wilderness resources would be protected; spring gentians would still flourish, and the Pennine merlin would still hunt the high ground, his habitat conserved. Success for the environmentalists will show that a balance can be struck. And if it can be done in the Pennines of England, why not elsewhere?

BREAKING NEW GROUNDS

There's certainly been no shortage of human development over the last thirty years. Scientists have challenged the very laws of nature, experimenting with genetics and bio-technology; technologists have taken humanity to the moon and sent machines to probe the solar system. We have hydro-electric and nuclear power, factory-farming and supersonic flight, wonder drugs, colour television, and the home computer.

With all the knowledge and skill behind these developments, no-one on earth need go cold or hungry; nobody need die in pain. Through transatlantic travel, and the media of international newsprint, signal, satellite, cable television and radio, we can observe the life-styles and customs of different countries at first hand. At the flick of a switch, nation can speak unto nation . . . and at least debate the insanities of another war. We have become residents of an international community, neighbours in a Global Village.

With these achievements we have the ability, the power, and clearly the energy and commitment to do immeasurable good. But it's all been too one-sided. The other side of progress doesn't look so good – the resource losses and environmental damage which have occurred in those thirty years have the combined potential to bring the 20th-century technological revolution and the complete human and planetary evolution to a sudden and nasty end. The check-list is dangerous and frightening. On the Doomsday Clock, it is a count-down to disaster:

TEN . . .   A third of the world's human population is on the verge of starvation. 28 children under 5 years die every minute from conditions relating to malnutrition and environmental pollution.

NINE . . .   A third of the world's arable land surface is turning into a desert due to human misuse. The world is losing an average of 8 tonnes of soil per hectare per year – but the maximum rate of soil replenishment is less than 5 tonnes per hectare per year, and nearly 21 million hectares of good land have been reduced to a state of agricultural uselessness.

EIGHT . . .   World fisheries have declined drastically since 1970 as a result of over-fishing. There has been no real attempt to conserve stocks and species.

SEVEN . . .   Our ever-dependence on genetically uniform mega-crops of maize, rice and wheat means that diseases can wipe out much of the crop, with catastrophic effects worldwide.

SIX . . .   World agricultural production has become over dependent on high energy inputs and on all kinds of fragile and wavering supports and subsidies: a precarious oil, chemical and capital fix.

FIVE ...   The world's population is out of hand. It has risen from 1000 million in the 1800s to 2526 million in 1950 and 4433 million in 1980. In less than forty years it will have nearly doubled again. And where are the resources to cope?

FOUR ...   We have already consumed more than half of the world's total reserves of coal, oil and natural gas which have fuelled the past 250 years of our success – and took around 300 million years to form. The resources which remain are less accessible and require more precious energy to extract.

THREE ...   Atomic power is now realized *not* to be the safe source of cheap, unlimited energy we were once told it would be.

TWO ...   What's left of the world's great tropical rainforests, now covering less than 6% of the earth's surface, are being destroyed. Since 1950, Latin

The second atomic blast at Bikini Atoll in 1946 produced a column of boiling water some 2,000 ft across and 5,000 ft high, and electric storms raged for days in the aftermath.

America has lost 35%, Central America 66%, South-East Asia 38% and Central Africa 52%. These are the world's greatest genetic banks, containing nearly half of all known plant and animal species, and they've been broken into.

ONE ... We have enough armaments to blow up the world many times over, and the stock-piles are still growing, increasing the ever-present risk of nuclear disaster by accident. We are now even talking about introducing nuclear and anti-nuclear weapons systems into space, the star wars dream of the munitions-mongers and the 'defence' scientists.

ZERO ... *BANG!* Put that lot together, throw in even a 'limited' thermo-nuclear war and there will be nothing left to say and no-one left to say it. Life on earth, if it survives at all, would be a sorry, sickly, poisoned thing.

Overleaf
Radio telescopes reflect the achievements of high technology and trans-globe communication. But are the right messages getting through?

As residents of the *global* village we have a daunting task at hand, but what a challenge! Thirty years on, the prospects for restoring a balance between development and the needs of the environment don't look wonderful. Can the tide of destruction be turned?

Mixed up with many of these problems is the threat to human development and world peace contained within the ever-widening gaps between the First and Third Worlds and between rich and poor. In the First World, the outmoded industrial dream of ever higher output, of constantly expanding levels of production, still lives on in the dreams of the new technologies. But as the saviour of progressive civilization they are clearly falling short.

Over 97% of the world's research and development budget is concentrated in parts of the northern hemisphere. In 1980 the world's ten richest countries were responsible for 83% of world production, while just three nations, the US, Japan and West Germany account for over 50%. In income terms, the First World, which has only a fifth of the world's population, receives two-thirds of all world income. The rest goes to the Third World and the eastern block combined, where *four-fifths* of the world's people live.

This gross inequality across the globe is at the epicentre of current world unrest. The trouble-torn nations of Africa, South America and South East Asia exist in a state of permanent economic crisis, with spiralling inflation (over 100% per annum in some countries), and mounting debts to the rest of the world from loans and interest charges. And just as wealth is concentrated in the First World, so poverty is concentrated in the Third World. A quarter of the world's population exists in a poverty trap characterized by malnutrition, illiteracy, disease, high infant mortality and low life expectancy.

This is disastrous for both the First and Third Worlds – for the developed world's economies rely on raw materials imported from the poorer nations, and nearly 50% of northern manufactured exports go to well-established Third World markets. Without trade and assistance, the economic systems of both the First and Third Worlds would suffer acute crisis. Economically, as well as ecologically, it is one interdependent world, but a world where all the systems are out of balance, tilting us in directions that we increasingly cannot handle. From out of the yawning chasm between rich and poor, haves and have-nots, First World and Third World, all kinds of horrors are emerging daily, in the shape of the burgeoning arms trade, international terrorism, inter-racial and inter-cultural atrocities.

HOME GROUNDS

The rich nations too, have their economic and social imbalances, their own 'Third World' problems of poverty, deprivation and unemployment. The gross inequalities on our doorsteps, particularly in our inner cities and once-thriving industrial areas, are reaching critical point, and are already beginning to explode in an increased cycle of violence and social tension. The industrial recession of the 1980s has destroyed lives, broken communities and undermined thriving, living human environments. Look at what's happened to Consett on the edge of the North Pennines, in County Durham. Thirty years ago a giant steelworks dominated both the place and the lives of the people who lived there. You could see the smelter works for miles around, a feature of the landscape and a nucleus of human activity. And if you didn't actually work in its furnaces or rolling mills, then you dug coal in the local mines or worked in the service industries which kept the whole place going and growing.

Right up until the 1970s the steelworks and ancillary industries, like many others across the industrial world, manufactured large amounts of goods for a burgeoning, Third World market. Something, however, went radically wrong: as the developing countries developed their own steel-making capacity, suddenly the world was producing too much steel. No-one could afford, or wanted to buy it, and Consett became a victim of its own success and of the proven effectiveness of its technologies, long since exported elsewhere.

The Consett steelworks were closed in 1980, the site bulldozed in 1981. In places where once there was industry and life there were now huge holes in the landscape. But there were also holes in the hearts and pockets of the people. In an area of traditionally high unemployment, 3500 people, nearly 40% of the local manufacturing workforce, were made redundant overnight. The knock-on effect on local services and other jobs was alarming. By 1984, the area around Consett had developed one of the highest unemployment rates in mainland Britain. Consett now has the aspect of a ghost town, empty, and down at heel. Its streets, once bristling with business and bustling family shopping establishments, have become a mecca for budget shopping stores, trading in cheap, shoddy manufactured goods for those who are down on their luck and lacking the prospect of new employment.

During earlier recessions in northern England, in the 1860s and early 1900s, you could always emigrate, as many of the Dales lead miners did—heading for the ore and mine fields of America and Canada. But now there is no escape from the grim realities of Consett, and in the 1980s its story is replicated in towns and cities throughout the industrialized world. We have entered a new phase in world history, the post-industrial revolution; where large-scale, labour-intensive industrial activity is becoming replaced by micro-processing. One man or woman at a computer terminal can now do the work of hundreds. Even Consett now boasts a number of high technology plants, including a chemical works which converts gas to a chemical wafer heralded as the next step forward from the silicon chip. But it has only a small workforce, and employment prospects are low.

It would be wrong to romanticize about the town's golden past. There were immense problems. Life around the steel works meant a long, hard, unremitting grind of tough work. There was pollution from the plant, and for the people who lived and worked there, there was little hope of planning for a long, healthy retirement. But the people did have roots. Generation after generation of family and close-knit community life had become focused in one place. Life evolved around the place of work. This was a place in which people understood the jobs they had to do and took a certain pride in doing them. They earned a weekly

wage, and within the limits of that wage they could plan to improve their life-style and the place in which they lived.

This sense of affinity with place, a feeling of belonging to and being a part of the local environment, its present and its past, is a feature of traditional human communities everywhere. It is a social and psychological condition, which brings together environment and human culture. The culture of Consett was built upon a working environment, in the same way that the cultures of the American Indian tribes were built upon their relationship to their natural environment. Near to Consett, among the hill farmers of the High Pennines, it is still known for the ashes of the old 'fell-men' to be cast after cremation upon the fell-sides where they made their daily living. Work, place, culture and surroundings, whether in industrial, agricultural or tribal communities, are all inextricably linked: they are all part of the environment as a whole. When this sense of belonging exists, it is one of the greatest assets of any society. Where it is still well-pronounced, as in the old communities of the Pennines and the north-east, the environment will continue to be respected as long as local economic and community life is sustained.

The exact opposite of this, the rootlessness characteristic of life on the margins of the world's city conurbations and of great population movements, can be a source of great social and psychological disorder, leading invariably to environmental vandalism of one kind or another. In the UK the re-settlement and re-housing of entire inner-city communities after the Second World War in custom-built newtown housing estates, like the vast Kirkby in Merseyside, laid the seeds of vandalism and environmental dereliction. Within a few years of resettlement, the youth of the uprooted population, lacking any affinity to their new home and existing in a formula-living plan which catered little for their cultural, community or economic needs, started to attack their physical surroundings. They defaced buildings, destroyed hedges and uprooted trees. In their alienation and frustration they turned on their own environment.

In the 1970s and 1980s when the new recessions started to bite deep and the newly-imported local factories closed one after another, the vandals went a step further. Mimicking the decay and the rot that had settled in around them, permeating to the heart of every household, they started to spoil their own nests, destroying houses and attacking the families that lived in them, their own people. Crime rates soared and frightened families moved out. Today, modern Kirkby is an urban wilderness where broken streets and vandalized parks provide only a windswept corridor for the doom and despondency in the hearts and minds of those who still live there. As we approach the last two decades of a century of unparalleled human progress, similar stories can be told of slum cities, industrial towns and new settlements the world over, in Chicago and New York, in Rio and Mexico City, in Bombay and Bangkok.

Consett, Durham – in happier days ... doomed, following crippling recession in its major industries, to become a ghost town plagued by unemployment.

Environmental vandalism due to rootlessness and a lack of identity with new surroundings has always been the negative face of pioneering, of the forging of new frontiers across the globe, whether through adventure, invasion or re-settlement. There has never been a species as disruptive as man on the move: with progress there has always come destruction, intentional or not. In history this was as true of the invasions of the Goths, the Turks and the Macedonians in the ancient world, as it was of the Europeans in the 18th and 19th centuries. And today it is the turn of Latin America, where developers and urban dwellers have started to invade the tropical forests, depleting resources that took centuries to accumulate, and by upsetting fragile local ecosystems have set in train a process of irreversible environmental change and decline.

As environments are destroyed so too are the people. The four million Indians that once inhabited the forests of the Amazon have been reduced in number to a few hundred thousand inside the last thirty years. With them has also gone a delicate equilibrium between man and the local environment which had been built up over the centuries.

With all new settlement, in the jungles of the Amazon, and across the spectrum of world history, the old relationships are lost for ever. We adjust to new ways of living, but the balance isn't quite right. There comes a point when the balance is so precarious that the very system it holds up collapses in upon itself, and everybody, everything lives on the edge of total atrophy. And these days, with our new adventures in progress, technology, power and weaponry we're in danger of upsetting more than a local equilibrium. Nationally and internationally, we're spoiling everyone's nest. Our environmental vandalism has gone global.

CHILDHOOD'S END?

We now travel back in time to the innocence and equilibrium of another era, the countryside of our own childhoods.

In the 'old days', the people of the industrial and urban revolutions and after, at Consett and elsewhere, did have their peaceful places away from the noise and the smells. Not far away from the dark satanic steelworks, mills and collieries, there existed a green and pleasant land of fields and woods, leafy glades, winding lanes and hedgerows. For in Britain and in much of industrial Europe in the early part of the 20th century, the countryside was a place of relatively free access, as long as you respected the local rules and conventions. And most people did – with the possible exception of the odd poacher! It was a haven of peace and solitude if you wanted it. And a place of living interest away from the gruelling rigours of a six-day working week.

In those early days, town and country, industry and agriculture, were bound together. And while the men of steel and coal could find solace, peace and recreation in the rolling countryside which fringed the towns, men and women of art and literature living mostly urban lives could find in the countryside great inspiration for noble works of creation. One of them, D. H. Lawrence, came from the Nottinghamshire coalfields, a background similar to that of the people of Consett, with heavy extractive industry set in the heart of rolling, rural landscapes. The countryside for Lawrence was a source of vital inspiration. He saw an almost blood-like liquid link between man and the natural environment. For him, human energy and natural energy were indivisible. The countryside was a vital source for the experience of freedom and creative inspiration to which he believed all human-kind were entitled. The leading character in his novel *The Rainbow*, provides the literary medium for one such vital vision, a vision of regeneration through nature and of a new millennium at hand:

> 'And the rainbow stood on the earth. She knew that the sordid people who crept hard-scaled and separate on the face of the world's corruption were living still, that the rainbow was arched in their blood and would quiver to life in their spirit, that they would cast off their horny covering of disintegration, that new, clean, naked bodies would issue to a new germination, to a new growth, rising to the light and the wind and the clean rain of heaven. She saw in the rainbow the earth's new architecture, the old brittle corruption of houses and factories swept away, the world built up in a living fabric of Truth, fitting to the over-arching heaven.'

Close links with nature are forged in childhood. But the countryside which provided the inspiration for the writers and painters of our growing-up, has changed beyond recognition and in a very short period of time. Believe it or not, a little over thirty years ago the British countryside had hardly changed from the days when the painter John Constable captured all that was best in the English landscape on canvas. The greatest changes have taken place within our own lifetimes.

Just take a short visit back through time to the countryside of a British childhood and then take a short walk through that same countryside today.

Where once there were wild-flowers, the chances are you'll now find a desert of perennial rye grass, green but gruesome in its uniformity. Since the 1950s, we've lost over 95% of the flower-rich meadows which once graced Britain's green and pleasant land. Every year, old footpaths are blocked with barbed wire, diverted or ploughed up. The fields have been re-designed and re-built, not for animals or plants or to accommodate human access, food for local markets, and a place for wildlife, but to make room for gigantic combines and cultivators. And as the European food mountains get bigger and bigger, so do the machines which serve them, to the extent that they have gobbled up over 120,000 miles of hedge since 1946. Nearly half our ancient woodland, composed of mature broad-leaved trees, bird- and insect-filled oak, elm, birch and lime has been felled since the Second World War, removed to create agro-deserts or dark black conifer plantations. In the past forty years we've destroyed as much as our forefathers did in 400 years. And we're still at it, at a faster rate than ever before.

Even the boggy bits are being drained and ploughed up in preparation for growing more crops and grass. Inside the last three decades we've ruined half of the traditional, over-wintering sites for the flocks of migrating birds which have graced our skies and standing waters for centuries. Many of their watering holes

The Merlin – threatened by the destruction of its habitat by modern man.

have been drained, reclaimed or poisoned. And up in the hills in that time, a third of Britain's upland heath and grassland has disappeared under the plough or a blanket of conifers.

Along with the destruction of these great wilderness habitats we have seen the eradication of large numbers of our most magnificent species, like our great birds of prey, our falcons and owls. Destroy habitats and you eradicate species. The point has been passionately made by Lord Melchett, a farmer and landowner, and President of Britain's Ramblers Association, an amenity body with a membership of over 35,000, founded to create access to the countryside for all.

'Conservationists are sometimes told not to be emotive about what is happening to our countryside. People talk of "improving wetlands", "converting" moorland, "bringing marginal land into production". The destruction of wetlands, moorland and flower meadows is something that should make us emotional. Take away a person's shelter and food, and they will die. The same is true for wildlife. Destruction of wildlife habitats involves the death of wildlife just as surely as if the plough share was ripping out the guts of a struggling golden eagle; as if the bucket on the dragline was being plunged into the back of a screaming hare.'[5]

The threat to Britain's wildlife isn't just through the physical destruction of habitats. Our modern crops, and thus of course all the surrounding habitats, are sprayed many times every year with a whole variety of chemicals. In fact today there are more than three thousand different sorts on sale, many of which are highly toxic to wildlife – in fact so toxic that aerial spraying isn't allowed (officially at least) on fields to which the public has access. Modern agriculture, through all its forms, chemical and technological, has sounded a death-knell for some of Britain's most beautiful birds and mammals, for the otter, the corncrake, the stone-curlew and the kingfisher, the dotterel and the goshawk. At one time common, these are now all species at risk which you are very unlikely to come across today.

Opposite
The rainbow symbol of hope over a still green and pleasant part of our land.

The destruction of the countryside is all done in the name of productivity and efficiency. But who benefits? We in the West have more food than we need, mountains of it being kept in European grain stores and silos, accumulating year after year. And there are grave doubts about the nutritional value and purity of the food we get by these methods. The people who traditionally lived on the land and by the land have had to leave. The agricultural labour force fell by 423,000 between 1950 and 1967, so that only 3% of the UK's working population remains on farms. Compare that with the situation in the middle of the last century when 92% of the country's labour force was employed in agriculture. Many small and part-time farmers, the creators of the original patchwork countryside, have gone out of business now and only an additional 1500 farms disappear every year. Farming in the UK gives full time employment to 400,000 people, less than all those out of work in the nation as a whole.

Increased unemployment on the land has had a disastrous knock-on effect in rural communities, particularly in the remoter areas. Village shops, post-offices and pubs are closing, transport and medical services are declining. Community facilities are falling apart through neglect and lack of use. And the villages are depopulating as the rural youth migrate to the towns and cities in (an often vain) search for jobs and a future.

In this depressing picture, First World truly meets Third World. For the decline of Britain's remoter rural areas since the war years, reflected at its worst in the abandoned buildings, closed schools and empty streets of the Pennine hill villages, can be compared to the rural decline afflicting large parts of Africa and South America, following the drift to the cities and shanty-towns by the dispossessed people of the rural areas. They too are in search of work and a place in the 20th century. The story is the same. But there is one major main difference: the scale and the terrible poverty, both urban and rural, which accompanies all population movements in the Third World.

The countryside is abandoned and dispossessed. It's not 'yours' or 'ours' anymore. But neither is it really the farmers'. The show is being run increasingly by large farm businesses and city institutions. And behind the growth of big farms are the banks, the agri-chemical and farm machinery multi-nationals. To many of these, we owe our livelihoods, but as large impersonal organizations they are sadly remote and out of touch with our other needs, for fresh air and freedom of access. Their concern for our wildlife is scant: their brief is simply to make money and create growth.

The overall result is bad news for Britain, a nation of gardeners, animal lovers, wildlife enthusiasts and walkers. In thirty years, the country's wildlife has had to run for cover, for the refuge of occasional patches of rough ground, for the edges of the great cereal plains, the hills and coastlines. A great wilderness heritage has been marginalized, shifted onto the sidelines of our lives on an increasingly over-polluted, over-populated island environment. What is left has to be contained in captive, controlled environments; in parks and zoos, on reserves and Sites of Special Scientific Interest (SSSI's). And even these are under constant threat from lack of finance, commercial exploitation, neglect, conflicting pres-

Industrial recession in the 1930s – a scene that fits all too easily into the 1980s.

Overleaf
A portrait of inner-city decline.

sures and interests, and in some cases from insufficient, badly integrated management controls. Because of the very industrialization of the countryside through modern agricultural development, there is now more true wildlife interest in parts of our urban and suburban areas, in our city parks and gardens, than in many rural areas. In recent years, some of Britain's wild animals have even deserted their original rural habitats in favour of the new homes being created for them within the urban waste-lands which have been steadily growing in our inner cities.

For most of us now our environment is thoroughly urban. Concrete, tarmac, bricks and mortar have been our natural surroundings for most of our lives. However there are many for whom the desperate attempts to ruralize the

high-rise living accommodation built by our planners and developers in the cities to house city immigrants and the old 'slum' communitues, whether Paris, Frankfurt, Bilbao, Merseyside, Glasgow or Newcastle, don't cut much ice. The reality behind this veneer is often faceless, lifeless desolation.

Frustrated by the 'industrial' barriers encountered on your walk in the country, you may have decided to take a relaxing bus-ride back through town for a quick inner look at the city.

If you live in the heart of urban north east England, in Newcastle-upon-Tyne, you'll find little aesthetic joy for your fare. After a few short stops past the leafy suburbs where the affluent live, your route will take you into limbo land. Here, the city centre is denuded of homes and suffers from declining public services as the private car dictates the shape of things. Our peculiar 20th-century homage to the motor car has led to us designing our cities around it at the expense of our needs as human beings. To bad design and to the autocracy of the car we owe much of our urban environmental degradation. These are major factors in the rise of urban squalor, of drug addiction, of increases in stress, trauma and crime. The improved technology, new engineering skills and desire for experimentation which succeeded the war years throughout Europe led to a building boom, and we reached for the skies with high-rise living. The results looked impressive at the time, even receiving architectural awards, but the 'economic' building materials used, cheap building techniques and the absence of the vital human factor in the new design technologies undermined the heights, and resulted in low-quality living. Those city skyscrapers still standing, are now centrepoints of despair. The time has indeed come, for our urban planners and designers, along with the rest of us, to come down to earth.

NEW FRONTIERS

Down to earth, and at the very bottom of the Pandora's Box which man and his technologies have opened on to the world, there is Hope. There is alive an international force and climate of opinion, an environmental 'movement', which almost alone seems to grasp the need to restore the equilibrium we have lost, to bring us back from the edge of destruction. The seeds of this were sown in the 1960s and it has grown rapidly since then, nurtured by the new scientific views and findings of ecologists and biologists and general systems theorists. There has even been help from the very bowels of the darkest of all our scientific endeavours, from nuclear and high-energy physics. Now flourishing, environmentalism grows from strength to strength, becoming a major political and cultural force throughout the western world.

Environmentalism carries with it an ancient credibility, it takes some of the best ideas from the dawn of history, from the tribal cultures and ancient philosophies of the Third World. These are blended together with modern technological know-how to create an enlivening fusion of influences from old and new. Even where there are nations new to history and still in the throes of becoming 'developed', green views have emerged. Environmental groups are springing up everywhere in the form of NGO's (non-governmental organizations), in places as far apart as Ireland, India, the South Pacific, Kenya, Nigeria, New Zealand and Alaska.

The successful spread of green ideas into our conscious and unconscious deliberations, growing daily in support and credibility even in the reactionary days of the 1980s, represents a turning point in the history of civilization. In the words of physicist and philosopher, Fritjof Capra, the growing strength of green world-views in world civilization, in thought, everyday behaviour, and even commerce, represents a new genesis in the history of human culture – 'The Turning of the Tide'. In the 1980s, environmentalism may be still a rustling in the political undergrowth of many nations. But it is a rustling to be reckoned with. The sinking of the *Rainbow Warrior* in Auckland Sound testifies to its effect upon the vested interests whose ambitions, if left unchecked, would allow us to lurch towards extinction.

At the very heart of the new environmentalism there nestles the spirit and good sense of conservation. This has ancient and noble beginnings. For the tribal societies of the old world, it was a fundamental fact of life. To survive and prosper you had to conserve your resources, respect and preserve the environment in which you lived. But conservation was for them not something consciously applied, it was instinctive. There was no separation between culture and nature, between the lives of men and the natural world around them. And for them that inter-dependence was fused with the omniscience of the spiritual or creator world, the very power which they believed guided their existence on the earth. Many tribal societies were organized along lines modelled upon nature, with subdivisions into groups of animal species and natural phenomena, into totemic clans of wolves, bears, eagles, grasses and skies. Each clan was considered as the descendant of a great spiritual animal or entity and each clan member took his name from the sights and sounds of the world around them. This is a pattern consistent to tribal societies the world over, from the aborigines of Australia, to the bushmen of the Kalahari, the Celtic peoples of Britain and Ireland and the Indians of the Brazilian Amazon.

This sense of unity with nature and the ethos of conservation and respect for living growing things is lyrically celebrated in the recorded speeches of the Red Indian. This is how a Lakota Sioux Indian, Chief Luther Standing Bear, saw the Indian's classical attitude to nature. The Indian

'Loved the earth and all things of the earth, the attachment growing with age. The old people came literally to love the soil and they sat or reclined on the ground with a feeling of being close to a mothering power. It was good for the skin to touch the earth and the old people liked to remove their moccasins and walk with bare feet on the sacred earth. The birds that flew in the air came to rest upon the earth and it was the final abiding place of all things that lived and grew. The soil was soothing, strengthening, cleansing and healing. Kinship

'White Calf', a member of a proud and ancient tribe that was broken by 'progress' and the thoughtless destruction of its land.

with all creatures of the earth, sky and water was a real and active principle. For the animal and bird world there existed a brotherly feeling that kept the Lakota safe among them and so close did some of the Lakotas come to their feathered and furred friends that in true brotherhood they spoke a common tongue. The old Lakota was wise. He knew that man's heart away from nature becomes hard; he knew that lack of respect for growing, living things soon led to lack of respect for humans too. So he kept his youth close to its softening influence.'[1]

Persecuted and hunted like the wild animals with which he identified, the Red Indian quickly became, to the great shame of American New World 'civilization', a relic of history, a 'species' without protection. However, in the early development in the Old World of that peculiarly disorderly and quite often uncivil type of human society we call 'civilization', we do find good examples of conservation, cultivated positively as a principle of good practice. We find it contained even in the folds of the First Agricultural Revolution. This probably took place in Asia Minor around 6000 BC, and at the very heart of this first of many great steps forward for 'progressive' humanity was the principle of fallow.

The observation of nature by early cultivators led to the discovery that if you purposefully allowed fields to lie fallow after a period of cropping, the soil became enriched and subsequent yields were improved. The land, allowed to naturally regenerate, to collect and conserve its energies, responded well to the hand and demands of man.

But as time and 'civilization' marched on, great pressures began to build up, threatening some of the most prized assets of the natural world. Some of the most powerful of world citizens became conscious of the need for conservation and established the world's first nature reserves. The world's first planned genetic reservoirs were tree parks in Babylon and Assyria, established in 1110 BC. And the first ever botanic garden was designed in Nineveh (in ancient Iraq) around 700 BC. In medieval England over 5 million out of a total of 37 million acres of land were set aside as hunting reserves. Sherwood Forest in Nottinghamshire, home of the legendary Robin Hood, once stretched over the entire land area of almost two present-day English counties. As well as providing home for the king's royal game, this great natural oak forest gave incidental protection to a vast range of indigenous plant, animal and insect species. Outside the forest these were becoming rare: Sherwood gave sanctuary to 'wildlife' of all kinds, animal plant and human.

Nearer to our own time, in the 17th and 18th centuries, conservation of flora and fauna became common cause and a part of science in Britain and the USA thanks to the growing influence of the earlier naturalists like Carolus Linnaeus and Gilbert White. Their work inspired Charles Darwin, leading eventually to the explorations of *HMS Beagle* and the publication of his *Origin of Species* in 1859. Those were the days when the first great national and international conservation bodies were launched: in Britain, the (later Royal) Society for the Prevention of Cruelty to Animals, in 1824; the Royal Society for the Protection of Birds (the RSPB) in 1889; the National Trust in 1893 and the Council for the Preservation of Rural England (the CPRE) in 1926. In the United States in 1865, an Act of Congress was passed to preserve the Yosemite Valley in California, and in 1872 the world's first National Park was created at Yellowstone in Wyoming. The first of the Audubon Societies, named after the great wildlife painter, was founded in the 1880s. The American Presidents Theodore and Franklin D. Roosevelt both saw conservation as a primary component in the development of water and timber resources. They also saw the preservation of wilderness for recreation and research as a cornerstone of the American way of life. The principle of unbridled access to the last of the country's great undeveloped natural heritage areas became as fundamental to the American Way of Life as apple pie, and something to be fought over.

Enthusiasm for nature and the delights of the natural world have never really strayed far from the sights of men and women of letters and leisure, but in the past it never really figured as a popular public, political and economic force. And even among the select few the power of conservation as an ideal has always ebbed and flowed with the tide of history and the relentless march of progress. Only when things seem to go too fast and begin to get a bit out of hand has conservation and the environment become a force of influence, a source of new ideas for society. It is at these times when the environment 'goes public'.

The 20th century has seen three such points, when the gates of public consciousness became open to the influences and concerns of the 'environment'. The First Wave, a sudden surge in public and political interest, coincided with the great re-think, the *fin du siècle* of the Victorian era, the time of the post-Darwin collectors and explorers, the reports of the anthropologists and overseas missionaries. It also coincided with rapid technological leaps forward, with improved systems of communication and the heyday of the British Empire. The Victorians had suddenly become conscious of the limits to pioneering, the finiteness of global resources and the existence of 'One World'. They also became conscious of the loss of amenity at home, the spread of their cities, their urban squalor and of the destruction of wildlife.

The Second Wave, followed the ending of the Second World War. In the post-war climate of internationalism, the first, truly international nature protection body, the IUPN (International Union for the Protection of Nature) was founded, in 1948. Its beginnings owed much to the support and encouragement of scientist Julian Huxley, then Director General of UNESCO, the United Nations Agency set up to promote international cooperation in the fields of education, science and peace.

Another UN agency, the FAO (Food and Agriculture Organization), was entrusted with the task of promoting the conservation and management of natural resources to alleviate world food shortage. In 1949, the UN itself held the very first international conference on the environment, the earth's resources and their conservation. In 1956, IUPN had a name change to IUCN (The International Union for Conservation of Nature and Natural Resources). And in 1961, it played a critical role in setting up the charitable World Wildlife Fund. With its headquarters established in Geneva, the WWF has since become possibly the most influential and respected international organization on the conservation scene.

In 1947, the Attlee Labour government in Britain passed the *Town and Country Planning Act*. Among other things this imposed limits to development in the rural environments encircling Britain's towns and cities. The idea of the Green Belt was born. In 1949, access to green space became an automatic right of every English citizen through the passing of another piece of enlightened environmental legislation, the *National Parks Act*. This created ten great National Parks in the upland areas of England and Wales. Some 13,600 sq km of the most beautiful and unspoilt countryside in Europe, including the Lake District, the Borders Country and the mountains of Snowdonia, were offered protection for posterity.

The incoming Conservative government also passed, in 1956, one of the world's first-ever pieces of anti-pollution legislation, the *Clean Air Act*. This put an end to coal-burning in the inner cities. The London smog, which had claimed many thousands of lives from lung disease and heart disorder, became a thing of the murky past. Decades of scrubbing later, the great buildings of London have only just been stripped of their unwholesome sooty overcoat and restored to their original stone-coloured splendour. Ironically also in 1956, science's first great 'clean' alternative to the burning of fossil fuels for energy was also unleashed upon the world. On 17th October, at Windscale in Cumbria, Queen Elizabeth II switched power from the four Calder Hall atomic fission reactors into the UK's National Electricity Grid. In a blaze of international publicity, the age of 'Nuclear power for peaceful purposes' was born. The following year, another, less publicized blaze took place at Windscale. A plutonium-producing reactor caught fire, releasing a large cloud of radio-active particles across the surrounding countryside. The great nuclear alternative hadn't remained 'clean' for long.

The Third Wave of interest in conservation and concern for the environment rolled ashore in the mid 1960s, and to an extent it has never really receded from this time. This wave was powered by two major winds of change in post-war industrial society. The first of these was the rapid growth in consumerism, in affluence, and in the effluence that came with it. The affluent expected a decent, open and clean environment in which to pursue the new leisure activities that they could afford for the first time – golf, sailing, rambling, swimming, touring, picnicking and gardening; they didn't want to swim in their effluent or have their scenic views of charming countryside despoiled by industrial agriculture. But the expectation of a clean and healthy environment at home also coincided with bad news from abroad. This was the second major wind of change, wafted in by rapidly improved international communications networks brought environmental catastrophes and the problems of the Third World right into the homes of ordinary people. The global imbalance was revealed. People could experience on television, in graphic second-hand, the sense of a race slipping gradually out of control of itself and its environment.

There was also a rapid rise in the number and scale of environmental accidents across the globe. In 1966 at Aberfan in Wales, a coal slag heap collapsed smothering the village school, killing 144 people and wiping out almost an entire generation of the village's children, 116 in total. In 1967, the oil tanker Torrey Canyon spilled 875,000 barrels of oil into the English Channel, polluting the sea and beaches for miles around, suffocating countless numbers of fish and seabirds. In 1969 there was a massive 77,000 oil barrel blow-out off Santa Barbara in California, causing widespread coastal pollution.

Worse accidents were to follow, but these were the headliners of the time, putting force behind the dire warnings of a new breed of scientific and ecological writers like Rachel Carson. Her 1962 book *Silent Spring* convinced an increasingly concerned American public that industrial and agricultural pollution of the environment and its wildlife, was not only ugly and unpleasant, but potentially catastrophic for human health. Environmental pollution, she graphically demonstrated, undermined the fundamental well-being of all life, it disturbed the delicate balance of nature. But it seemed that the tide of destruction which humanity had created for itself was waiting offshore. A build-up of global pressures, over-population, pollution, famine and the threat of a nuclear holocaust seemed ready to engulf us all. But the new mood of environmentalism was building up a strong counter-tide, a turning point in our consciousness of the

problems, and a new sense of the responsibility and vision needed to stem the flood of destruction.

The Apollo space missions of the 1960s brought home to the world the incredible beauty and perfection of the global environment. From the perspective of outer space, there *was* only 'One World'. The mind-expanding pictures of earth taken from the spacecrafts, illuminated the globe as a truly living entity travelling through space. The world could be seen by millions as a time and travel machine for humanity, fuelled by vulnerable and inter-dependent resources of soil, water and air. And a new breed of thinkers, writers and scientists appeared on the horizon to offer future tools and concepts for the operating manual of Spaceship Earth. Works like Paul Erlich's *The Population Bomb*, Alvin Toffler's *Future Shock*, Theodore Roszak's *Person/Planet*, and the writings and lectures of Ralph Nader, Barry Commoner and Buckminster Fuller exercised a major influence on the social and scientific thinking of the new generations of spaceship operators. Many of these new environmental spokesmen did not simply focus on the problems and the mistakes, they suggested practical alternatives, new ways of providing for our needs which would not destroy the environment.

By the late sixties, an entire generation of youth in the USA and Europe was experimenting with the possibilities of inner space. Their controls were set, not for more affluence and consumer goods but for the heart of the universe itself. Out of this millennarian culture of music, meditation, eastern philosophies and alternative politics, there emerged the sights and sounds of a new global spring-time, the ideology of 'Whole Earth'.

Since Judaeo-Christian times, humankind has been viewed in western culture

Mothers of the Kumaon Himalaya honouring their Earth Goddess as she returns to the earth after summer in the fields.

Hindu temple sculpture of Earth Goddess, Mother of Life.

as separate from nature. The natural environment, we have always been told, was there to serve our purposes, to be 'subdued' and exploited for our own uses. The elements, the animals and even womankind were all part of the patriarchal plan, the creation of a male and masterful god. But in the new politics and philosophies, humanity was seen not as above and apart, but as an integral part within a whole range of inter-connecting and independent systems within systems. Man's futile attempts through history to completely bend nature to his will has created a disorder that was undermining the balance within and between all other natural and global systems.

In contrast to the linear thinking and short-sightedness of the scientists and politicians who saw no limits to progress or growth, the 'whole-earthers' argued that we had to live within our limits, paying heed to the delicate balances of the world in which we live. They believed that the disorders of pollution, overpopulation and destruction could only be remedied by adopting a systematic approach to human and technological development. This could be done through the adoption of the principles of conservation, and through the exploration and application of smaller-scale, locally-based and locally-controlled, more manageable and more 'organic' technologies of energy production, food-growing, home building, and resource utilization.

Enrichment and support for the visions and basic principles of the Whole Earth Ideology and for the fresh expressions and fears of sixties youth came from other publications which followed in the early seventies. Most notable of these was Schumacher's *Small is Beautiful*, the harbinger of a new spring in adult economic and social thinking. Schumacher argued that at the very root of the world's economic and environmental problems was our obsession with 'things big', with creating giant organizations and increased technological specialization. Taking inspiration from the economics of ancient Buddhism and the writings of Mahatma Gandhi he proposed as a solution, a system of 'Intermediate Technology', including local-level production systems, smaller working units and shared ownership. Schumacher took the emphasis away from the product and towards the person: 'an economics as if people mattered.' Other publications of the early seventies continued to emphasize the scale of the gathering environmental crisis, in particular, the Club of Rome's *The Limits to Growth* and the Ecologist's *A Blueprint for Survival*. As in the 1940s, environmental concern became international: conservation and the environment became the subject of a whole series of UN and international conventions. These culminated in the 1972 UN Conference on the Human Environment at Stockholm. The proceedings of this historic meeting have been setting agendas for environmental resolutions and legislation in nation states well into the eighties.

In Britain during the 1960s and 1970s a whole new range of conservation and anti-nuclear organizations came into being, including the local County Conservation Trusts, the British Trust for Conservation Volunteers and the Conservation Foundation. In 1969 in America, Friends of the Earth was founded by David Brower and there are now branches in many European countries. Greenpeace, originally known as the 'Don't Make a Wave Committee', gathered strength after it successfully forced the cancellation of a nuclear test on the Aleutian Islands by sailing a boat with a full crew on board into the middle of the test zone. Greenpeace has been making many major waves ever since. The world's largest-ever demonstration against nuclear power – 75,000 people, took place in Washington after the nuclear accident at Three Mile Island, Harrisburg, when a cloud of radio-active gas escaped from the reactor and polluted the local atmosphere.

Since those heady days there have been many headlining conservation campaigns; at the Franklin River in Tasmania, at Murora Atoll in the South Pacific, over mega-dam projects in South America, Britain and Austria. There have been more chemical and radiation accidents, some causing large-scale environmental pollution, some involving tragic loss of life, at Flixborough in England, at Seveso in Italy, at Bhopal in India and Chernobyl in the USSR. There have been reams upon reams of government reports and research programmes and an endless stream of public inquiries on environmental developments. In 1980, with only two more decades to go before that monumental milestone the year 2000, two of the most important strategic documents of the 20th century were published. The first of these was the findings of the international Brandt Commission. This pointed to the dangers of ignoring the global imbalance which kept the First World rich while the Third World starved. It argued that we ignored this economic dis-equilibrium at our peril. It also warned that the ecological problems and resource depletion caused by rapid population and industrial growth in the Third World could tip us all over the edge of sustainable existence.

The second major report produced in 1980 was the World Conservation

Strategy. Sponsored in part by the IUCN and the World Wildlife Fund this was the first document of its kind: a coherent strategy for the maintenance of the world's ecological systems, its forests, soils and seas, intended to ensure the preservation and sustainable use of genetic diversity and natural resources. According to the WCS, environment and development were not incompatible, but inter-dependent. The pursuit of development, with the environment in mind, it argued, alone provided us with the means to service the crumbling body-work of *Spaceship Earth*, to 'Save the World'.

A new scientific view has now emerged which not only underwrites the common sense of the whole-earthers, but jumps the millennia to take us right back to conservation's starting points; the tribal eye-view of the cosmos and man's place in it, and the earthly reality of Asia Minor's fertile fallow fields. In 1979, a British atmosphere chemist, Dr James Lovelock, came up with a theory which he called *Gaia: A New Look at Life on Earth*. Lovelock had for most of his career, worked for the British government studying gaseous systems in outer space for signs of organic life. But with his *Gaia* hypothesis he came down to earth with a bang, shattering in the process a whole series of scientific conventions about the workings of *Spaceship Earth*. Using conventional scientific methods of data collection and analysis, Lovelock observed that the Earth's biosphere, the envelope of gases which lie between the surface of the planet and the vacuum of outer space, controls both the temperature on the Earth's surface and the composition of the atmosphere. This led him to argue that

> 'living matter, the air, the oceans, the land surface were parts of a giant system which was able to control temperature, the composition of the air and sea, the pH of the soil and so on, as to be optimum for survival of the biosphere. The system seemed to exhibit the behaviour of a single organism, even a living creature.'[6]

To the mechanistic eyes of many fellow scientists, Lovelock's view was heretical, almost quasi-mystical, but the logic and methodological soundness of his arguments were indisputable. The implications of his *Gaia* hypothesis were equally hard to counter, but equally hard to swallow. For through his science, Lovelock had realized something that the American Indians and the Buddhists had always taken for granted – that our common environment was a single dynamic entity, a self-sustaining, self-stabilizing, living, breathing thing. He called his concept *Gaia*, after the Greek Goddess, the Mother of Earth and all living things, the womb of the cosmos, source of beginnings and the place of endings.

In the concept of *Gaia*, ancient ethics meet modern standards, myth meets science. It also invites us to confront our own responsibilities towards a common environment; to care for earth because its stability is our stability, its health and welfare is ours. Destroy the constituent living systems – air, water, soils and forests, and we destroy ourselves. With our ability to destroy our life-support systems, our forests, seas, atmosphere and natural habitats and our capacity to wage thermo-nuclear war we are placing all life under threat. As we near that

point, a breaking point, it is clear that the environmental movement has never been stronger.

In the 1980s the world over, the environment has become a major item in every political agenda, a primary concern of voters everywhere. In Europe, the main political parties have started to take stock and are all vying with one another for their share in the 'green vote'. There are Green parties in all the western democracies, providing a loud rustling in the undergrowth which is eating away at the confidence of the old established order. The seeds of discontent and the desire for a second spring in the sixties have borne fruit. Conservation has at last found its political summer and if things continue to grow, it looks like being a long hot one for everybody.

As we travel forwards on our environmental journey there will be many chances to see the vital and timely green growth of the Green Movement in action. So far, from where it started in the watersheds of the High Pennines, our journey has taken us across country and into the city, back through time to our childhood, and forward to the global outposts of human progress and development, and to the new frontiers of the Green Movement. Now we make a temporary stop at the very bottom of that high watershed in the heart of industrial Tyneside, to see some local green action and to a little living system in a place where children still play.

Nowadays, almost any school child can tell you that the pace and quality of life in any observable living system down to the smallest of little ponds is controlled by an interlinked chain of resources, energy, minerals and the genetic potential of re-cycling and re-use. If you break any step in that chain of life, the whole system begins to slow down and collapse. What applies within your local pond, also applies to a region, a country and ultimately the whole world.

One small pond which contains a message for politicians everywhere occurs right in the heart of urban Tyneside, right in the middle of planning limbo-land. This pond is the centre of a tiny nature park which fringes the Benwell public housing estate. It was put there by local youngsters with the help of conservation volunteers. They have planted it out with aquatic plants like marsh marigold, yellow iris, purple loosestrife, and fringed it with a damp-loving belt of alder, willow and aspen. Around the pond is a range of habitats for plants and animals, including a native grassland meadow, wild flower beds, hedgerows and a varied native woodland of oak, ash, pine and hazel, mixed in with native shrubs like field maple, crab apple, bird cherry and a gloriously aromatic honeysuckle.

Already the park has attracted goldfinches, and house martins and kestrels – birds not seen in this part of the city for generations – and in the summer the area is alive with caterpillars, burnet moths and large white butterflies. The place is simply teeming and brimming with life and beauty, providing a haven amidst the city turmoil, a paradise of colour and texture among the urban greys and blacks. It is a tremendous project: it has brought the local community together, given city children a sense of nature in the city and created green hope where before there was only a wilderness of derelict properties and soul-less housing development.

Two years ago that pond in Benwell was just a dream. Now it is reality, thanks to the local people. Their environment is now a more beautiful, more interesting place. What has been done at a local level here could easily be achieved in other spheres. Indeed there is one experiment not far from Benwell which does pave the way: the Byker Wall housing development. Here, there is high-density living without the problems of high rise: people live in well-designed, yet futuristic homes using a variety of materials, set in an open environment with shrubs and flowers providing a diversity of colour and texture. The environment is user-friendly, and there's no graffiti or vandalism to be seen anywhere.

So planners, architects and builders can sometimes get it right. We do have an enormous range of materials available to build attractive communities, to make our living and working environments more exciting and enjoyable, to add enormously to our well-being. Imaginative design which incorporates nature, a sense of open-ness and a touch of green, doesn't have to imitate the design of hi-tech super stores. To be effective, the design and development of our homes, our domestic environments, our immediate living systems, need only to be simple to be sound, to be small to be beautiful. If the technology we use to build our living room demands less of the exotic imported resources but more locally-available products and techniques, then we are not depleting the global village's current stock of supplies so rapidly. We are giving them time to conserve and renew.

Benwell and Byker are down-to-earth, small-scale achievements which you might say are dwarfed by the problems and environmental pressures afflicting the global village. But their small-ness and their simplicity is their strength. They show a green-sight and they illustrate positive green action. They show that conservation begins at home, in conserving local resources, in improving our own living room, our own environment. Their example is an example for the global village. And they demonstrate a vital message for us:

'Think Globally, Act Locally.'

2 FUEL STOP

HAVE WE GOT THE ENERGY?

The world market prices of our primary sources of energy – the fossil fuels of oil, coal and gas – may go up and down, but our consumption is consistently high. At present rates, we will have used up most of our resources by the middle of the next century. We pay a high environmental price for our excessive consumption too, in such forms as oil pollution and acid rain. But these are nothing compared to the environmental, economic and social costs of nuclear power.

Our environmental journey takes us to the power bases, from coal to plutonium (named after Pluto, Greek God of the Underworld) and the product of an unholy energy pact made with some very dark forces. We look at safer alternatives, the clean, fresh power of the sun, wind and sea. And we take stock of the green potential of biomass and the re-cycled strength of energy from conservation.

BATHING IN ENERGY

This stage of our journey gives us the occasion to check up on Spaceship Earth's *fuel supply. Before exploring current stocks and future alternatives, let's check up on our ultimate source, and set the controls for the heat of the sun.*

Even when the sun doesn't shine directly on us, we're bathing in it. For all the energy contained in coal, oil and gas is ultimately solar energy, which has become trapped over time in the cells of these fossil fuels. Sunshine thankfully is free, but the energy supplied to us through the diminishing stocks of fossil fuels isn't.

It wasn't always like this: remember the days when coal was plentiful and cheap, we had plenty of energy to burn, and even some to waste? Mind you, our pattern of energy consumption wasn't as convenient as it is these days. Remember the palaver of bath-time in the old days – before the advent of immersion heaters and plumbed-in baths?

It used to take up the whole evening. You had to heat up the water and the room before you could even take your clothes off. Once you were in you had to keep the water adjusted exactly right. And it was all very, very inefficient, with the fire boiling you down one side, while a draught of cold air from under the kitchen door froze you down the other. Then all that lovely warmed-up air just

The sun – ultimate source of all our energy.

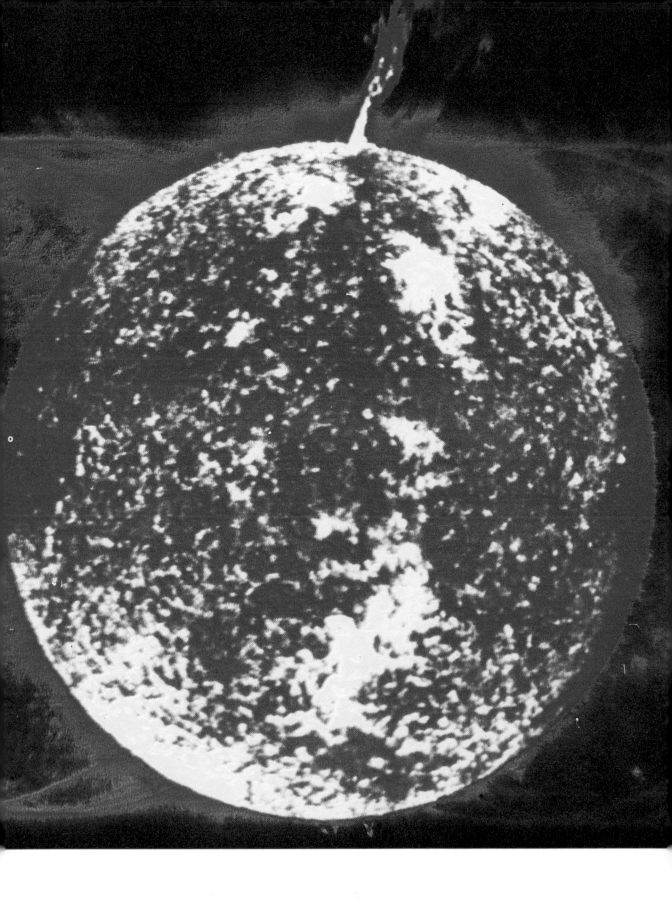

rushed to escape up the chimney — warming not you or the house, but the outside — what a waste! If you could see this scene through an infra-red movie camera which makes heat visible by colour, you would see waves of white where all the heat is — on the fireside and going up the chimney and waves of cold blue on the side facing the door. The blue wave is the dominant one, a big mass of blue swirling around the door, across the floor, past the bath, up the chimney and out into the environment.

Since the days when our parents and grandparents were using tin tubs we've come a long way. Technology has developed to allow us to use energy more efficiently — in other words to get more heat — or work out of it. In fact, that old tin tub you might have been using in the thirties is probably lying rusting on some heap somewhere — more energy wasted.

The house you lived in might also have been knocked down, and if it was done by one of those old steam shovels — a monument to energy inefficiency — even more energy would have been wasted.

These days that job would be done much more efficiently using an excavator, running not on coal, but on another type of fossil fuel: diesel. Much less noisy, less polluting, more energy-efficient, you might think ... but is it? It's still pretty noisy, there's a lot of wasted heat, and there's still some nasty-looking blue-black stuff sneaking out of that exhaust pipe. And when you add all that to diesel fumes coming from the lorries which take stuff from the digger, *and* the exhaust from the foreman's flash new car, you can see that even pulling down an old house involves a lot of energy, mess and waste.

Home, sweet home, for most of us in the developed world nowadays, is likely to be much more modern, and you would think more energy-efficient. Bath-time is sheer luxury: no draughts, nice warm home, plenty of piped, hot water. And it's all done at the flick of a switch. Even lazing in the bath we're surrounded by gadgetry designed to do all kinds of things from cleaning our teeth to polishing our toenails. And everything's powered by electricity ... It's wonderful stuff, no mess, no pollution, and no fuss — except perhaps when you come to pay the bill! But, wait a minute, what happens at the other end, the place where all this wonderful electricity is produced? Here we find energy factories, huge plants converting energy from coal, or oil into electricity. In fact, they're pretty noisy, smelly and dirty: look at those great chimney stacks billowing smoke full of sulphur and nitrous oxide gases into the atmosphere; and those great cooling towers absorbing all the heat that's wasted during the burning process which creates the electricity.

Two thirds of the energy contained in the glowing fuel which fires the turbines in those huge hot-houses is lost. That leaves a paltry one third of the total energy released from the oil or coal to provide our electricity. This is what physicists (with their unique ability for communicating scientific facts to us in everyday language) term, a 'thermo-dynamically inefficient' process — in other words, it's wasteful. Those huge power plants and furnaces are just larger and less attractive versions of the coal fire in the cottage: but the waste and everything else is less personalized because it arrives on someone else's doorstep. In fact, we end up using the surface of the earth and its atmosphere as dustbins for the unwanted products of the power stations . . . and they're no more efficient than the steam shovel we used to knock our old house down! Removing the process of energy production from our houses to these gigantic energy plants doesn't do away with the problems: we and our environment still end up footing the bill.

In the old days, coal was the major source of energy in the Western World. It fuelled the main thrust of the Industrial Revolution and two World Wars. Where we live in the North East, it fashioned a whole culture of mining communities, cloth caps, colliery wheels and union activities. Pitheads and pitheaps dominated the landscapes of the coastal coalfields and dominated the lives and the lung-conditions of those who lived there. Coal – rocks of compacted vegetation laid down in the hot, swampy carboniferous era some 300 million years ago – was then king. Those regions and countries with coal deposits and the technology to mine them had their own energy castles. Standing on piles of coal, we manned the ramparts of international industry and world development.

But that's all changed now. Coal is more expensive to acquire than other forms of fossil fuel, like oil and gas, and less flexible as a source of fuel and power. Currently it provides only 26% of the world's total energy supply; as opposed to 56% from oil and gas, 2% from hydro-electric power; 14% from fuelwood, charcoal and biomass and other renewable sources; and 2% from nuclear power. But if we use coal as a measure of our energy consumption, you would learn that each one of us uses an average 420 tonnes of coal in a lifetime. We use it for heat and light, to grow food and manufacture all the things we use in a lifetime from nappy to coffin. Some is used as the raw material for plastics, drugs, chemicals and other things which make our 20th-century lifestyle possible. Coal is precious stuff, because like all fossil fuels it is non-renewable: once it's all used up, that's the end; there's no more. Coal is so precious you would think that we wouldn't waste it. But the facts of daily life are different . . . it takes the energy equivalent of three sacks of coal to keep each one of us going for a week. And because of the inefficient way we live and the inefficient processes we use, two of those bags are completely wasted; spent, useless energy, a coal spill at the bottom of our energy pile. We burn up the equivalent of a quarter of the remaining sack just travelling round the place. You can see that our life styles are thermo-dynamically ultra inefficient!

Come with us on a trip from London to South America using all the transport facilities available and you'll see exactly what we mean:

Leg one involves getting through yet another traffic pile-up, crawling over the M40 'fly-over' looking for escape routes and burning up lots of energy getting annoyed with everyone else and breathing fumes of suffocating hydrocarbons from thousands of chugging exhausts every time we open the window. The car's energy-consuming air-conditioning doesn't really help, it just recirculates tired old air and fumes. All that petrol is consumed like it's going out of fashion and we're getting nowhere fast. Consider how much energy went into making this car

that's so amazingly inefficient in using the fuel it consumes. The average car only gives us thirty miles of transport to the gallon – even less in urban driving and less still in a pile-up! And it's only carrying three people, you, me and him . . . it's crazy. Let's park the car and get the bus!

In energy terms, buses make much more sense. One vehicle carries lots of people at only seven miles per gallon – that's 112 passenger miles per gallon, and there's company if you want it. Buses are three times more efficient in passenger-carrying terms than cars. You'd think that governments would encourage transport by bus, designing our roads and traffic flows accordingly, making the fares cheap, and services comfortable, frequent and reliable. But the opposite is the case, and if you are living in a rural area in the 1980's the chances are you haven't seen a bus for years. In England's countryside the bus has joined the peregrine falcon and become an endangered species.

As the crow flies though, we're better off getting off the bus at this stop and catching the train from Paddington Station to near the airport.

This is a quick, clean way of getting both people and baggage, feet and freight from point A to point B. And electric trains are the most efficient way of travelling of them all – the cheapest form of passenger transport. A three-car electric train will carry fifty passengers at an astonishing one and a half miles per gallon, fifteen times cheaper than the car. To add a touch of romance and comfort to a journey, you also can't beat the train. Yet in the First World less and less rolling stock is being built and every year more tracks and sleepers are being taken up than being laid down.

We're near the airport now. For the final leg of this part of our journey there's no better mode of transport than the dear old bicycle.

The bike is still the most efficient way to travel anywhere in the globe. All the power it needs is contained in the porridge you had for breakfast. Even if you take into account the energy that went into making this bike, you can still get the equivalent of 1000 miles to the gallon. The bike is clean and healthy, and gives you fifty times more miles per gallon than the plane we're just about to miss – unless we run.

In fact we have plenty of time – to wait at least – there's a large queue of jet aeroplanes waiting to take off, all full of hopeful holidaymakers heading for the sun and for the pleasure of not having to use any energy at all – at least to keep warm. In energy terms, aeroplanes are reasonably efficient: the higher they fly, the less fuel they consume. But it's still energy all the way. Because almost everything you're supplied with on the plane uses up fossil fuels. From the seating to the lavatory bowl, the plastic panelling on the cabin ceiling to the plastic tray on your lap with all those dinky little plastic knives and spoons in their see-through wrapping. It's all disposable, high-energy technology in this throw-away world we live in.

Opposite
Cooling towers in the north of England – two thirds of the energy contained in these hot-houses goes up in smoke – it's only the last third that produces our electricity.

Pause for a moment to consider the energy equation over most of the earth's surface, in those countries over which our plane to South America could be crossing. Every five minutes we spend travelling in a jet burns up the same amount of energy that one person from the Third World countries down below would use in a whole year. They too require supplies of energy to cook and keep warm like the rest of us. But for over a third of the world's population, and for most people of the Third World, that energy is provided by wood. A bit primitive, you might think, but the fact is that wood is a renewable resource, and doesn't cause heavy atmospheric pollution. Unfortunately, in most places, wood is being used up faster than it is being grown. This depletes the resource, forcing the people to look for other alternatives – or else do without – an alternative which has appalling consequences – for much of the food they have is useless unless cooked.

The jet has now landed at São Paolo Airport and we're in the Third World, in the heart of South America, vegetating by the hotel swimming pool.

The air is buzzing with the hum of insects and a warm wind is wafting through the tropical trees which fringe this little oasis of luxury and consumerism. It is hot, in fact it's so hot that they've turned on the air-conditioning full blast – and here come the ice-cold drinks to finish the job. We're expending no energy at all keeping warm. But wait a minute! What about the energy that's spent keeping us cool? And where's that coming from in a country like Brazil? You've guessed it. Just over the hill on the other side of town there's a nuclear power station, one of four Pressurized Water Reactors (PWRs) in the country. These were bought in from America and West Germany swelling the enormous national debt of $100 billion: lucky old world banks, think of all that interest.

Brazil is the South American country with the greatest number of hungry people, and yet sugar cane, a food crop, is harvested to produce the bio-fuel ethanol, which is burned to provide energy and fuel motor cars. And if you think we have a problem of car-congested cities, you should see the highways of São Paolo. They are chock-a-block with cars which sit all day in the worst traffic jams in the world. The one-way highway systems quadruple the journey distance across the city, and burn up large quantities of valuable bio-fuels grown on land which could be used to grow food for starving Brazilians. What is more, in order to pay off their national debts they are exporting more and more of the foods they produce to the rich, over-stuffed countries who lent them the money in the first place. It's just crazy – enough to make you get back on that plane and set the controls for the heart of damp cold old England!

Not content with deriving large amounts of our own energy supplies from resources which belong to the people of the Third World, we're exporting back to them energy-generating technologies quite inappropriate to local conditions and harmful to their environment. Worse than that, if their consumption patterns reached the same level as ours, the world's stock of energy resources, renewable and non-renewable, would be unable to keep up with demand, and severe shortages would quickly follow. This in turn would undermine overnight the already precarious trade and exchange system upon which all the nations of the world currently depend.

But in many respects, the energy holiday is already over: the earth's vital energy resources are, as we write, facing an inevitable crisis in the years which lie ahead. All over the world, we're burning up energy like there's no tomorrow, and tomorrow's world is going to be tough unless we get a grip on the way we're using up our resources.

It has been estimated that if we use up our available resources of fossil fuels at the current rate, with no increase in world consumption, then our coal, oil and natural gas will last for only 650 years, up to 2636 AD. That's fine for us but cold comfort for our children's children in the 21st century.

All the signs are that world energy consumption is unlikely to stay static: it is going to rise, and rise rapidly. Not just in the developed countries, but all over the globe. As little as a 2% annual increase in world consumption could mean that fossil fuels will run out within 124 years. A 5% increase would mean that they'd run out even quicker, by 2047, in just over sixty years. Compared to past patterns, a 5% increase would be modest. And even if we're being too doomy and gloomy, and the fossil fuels don't run out, or we are able to tap the extra reserves which are much more expensive to retrieve (using more energy in the process), then another equally depressing scenario is likely. A limited 5% annual increase in energy consumption up to the year 2000 would not sustain even moderate economic growth; would not lift the burden of poverty in the developing world; and would increase the tension and competition for fossil fuels that already exists between nations.

But, you will say, what about nuclear power, the high technologists' answer to the dying era of fossil fuels? The nuclear industry argues that it gives freedom from dependence on the world's old energy supplies. But in fact uranium, the raw material of nuclear reaction, is itself a non-renewable resource. Known easily-mined reserves are expected to run out within seventy years, by 2056. Even if we could make nuclear energy safe and re-assure people everywhere, it is not a renewable source of energy. There are even limits to the exploitation of the atom.

Even if all these official predictions prove eventually to be inaccurate, we still invite major problems on our heads if we continue not just the same pattern of consumption but also the same distribution of consumption. The developed countries use 100 times more energy per head than the developing countries. The Third World, in fact, only consumes about 12% of all commercial energy, and this is concentrated among only sixteen countries. The Brandt Report gave us a hierarchy of usage among a selection of nations: One American uses as much commercial energy as two Germans or Australians, three Swiss or Japanese, six Yugoslavs, nine Mexicans or Cubans, sixteen Chinese, nineteen Malayans, fifty-three Indians, 109 Sri Lankans, 438 Malians, or 1072 Nepalese. Fortunately, the partridge in the pear tree is self-sufficient in energy production and consumption, like the rest of the natural kingdom. But the tale of global imbalance becomes even sorrier when we realize that the entire fuel consumption of the Third World for all purposes, only slightly exceeds the petrol the First World burns in its cars, lorries and buses.

That global imbalance is a potential time-bomb in terms of world tension, and there is already hot competition for the depleting and more inaccessible resources. If we help the Third World to develop our models of consumption and living standards – which is after all the primary goal of all overseas development programmes – more and more nations will join the energy foray. It is our moral duty to help improve standards and eradicate poverty everywhere. But we must question whether it is our duty to encourage them to mortgage their futures by joining us in either creating further tiers of energy imbalance or in depleting the world even further of its entire energy resources.

FUEL FOR THOUGHT

Back to the present, there is another major problem with burning fossil fuels and using uranium. All this affects the environment directly, both locally and globally – the process causes pollution and dangers to public health. The environmental record of the coal industry for example has been a sorry one ... smog, blackened buildings, devastated landscapes, pit-heaps, polluted rivers, miners with broken health, and a long history of pit tragedies caused by pockets of gas and collapsed tunnels. In recent years, working and safety conditions for some coal miners has been vastly improved, and in many areas the broken landscapes of pit-heaps and open-cast quarries are currently being restored by environmentally sensitive local authorities. The most intractable problem which

London's 'pea-souper' smogs are a thing of the past. 1980s-style pollution is less visible ... but a more insidious and deadly power.

thus remains is the direct pollutants – a nasty list of wastes including sulphur oxides, heavy metals like lead, mercury and cadmium and cancer-inducing compounds like polycyclic hydrocarbons. No-one knows just how these materials behave in the environment, whether they simply diffuse and decay naturally or whether their effect is cumulative and they cause long-term toxic build-ups in the biosphere.

But in global terms possibly the most threatening emission from coal and other fossil fuels is a gas we all produce – carbon dioxide, CO_2 for short. Coal is the worst culprit, releasing 25% more CO_2 than oil and 75% more than natural gas for every unit of heat produced. Some scientists argue that an accumulation of CO_2 in the upper atmosphere at the current build-up of some 0.4% every year has the effect of warming the world's climate.

Well we could all do with that, you might think, but a dangerous environmental consequence is possible from this, the so-called 'Greenhouse Effect'. Increased levels of CO_2 in the atmosphere act like the walls of a greenhouse, trapping the solar heat which gets in through the glass and is bounced off the floor and plant beds and the tomatoes, so up goes the temperature. Any pleasure we might get from an estimated increase in world temperature of 3% above normal in the years to come, would be undermined by the prospect of large sections of the polar ice-caps melting, causing widespread coastal flooding around the globe, and endangering the livelihoods of the two-fifths of the world's population who have their homes by the sea.

There are also large-scale, but more localized environmental dangers associated with the widespread industrial processes in which oil and gas are involved. Natural gas, when mixed with air forms an explosive mixture which can be ignited by a spark. Every day there are smaller accidents like this in homes and near burst pipes – one careless match or a thoughtless smoker and the environment combusts like a car engine. In almost every major city of the western world there are oil, gas and subsidiary chemical installations capable of unleashing terrible destruction in the event of an accident. The Bhopal disaster in India in 1984, during which 2500 people lost their lives, and many more were injured or blinded for life, is the worst example in history; but depressingly, it will not be the last. Have you ever counted the number of oil-based chemical time bombs which are located in the vicinity of your home?

It's also a sobering thought that the transportation of liquefied natural gas and chemicals across the roads, oceans and railways of the earth also poses environmental dangers. The energy content of a tanker of liquid gas is as great as that of a nuclear bomb: a collision or terrorist attack on a tanker in a port could have disastrous consequences.

There is another more insidious type of pollution – acid rain. Exhaust pipes and towering chimneys pour some 90 million tonnes of sulphur dioxide and nitrous oxide into the atmosphere every year. Everything that goes up must come down, and these pollutants are no exception. Coming into contact with clouds of water vapour, they form dilute solutions of nitric and sulphuric acids which fall as rain – acid rain.

Acid rain is pollution that knows no boundaries, and recognizes no international conventions. Gases carried by winds across continents from industrial conurbations meet rainclouds everywhere, falling far from their source and concentrating in the areas of highest rainfall, often on uplands and remote rural areas. Here, acid rain accentuates an existing acid imbalance created by high rainfall and acid-loving coniferous trees which thrive in acidic peaty soils. The conifers, washed in acid rainfall and wafted with wind-borne dry acidic deposits, intensify the acidity in the soil beneath them. The resulting run-off creates a deadly scour which can drastically affect the quality of the water flowing through and from the catchment.

Forest policy across the developed world has encouraged mainly fast-growing conifers leaving even less room for the broad-leaved hardwoods which originally thrived on the same soils. *'Grow more softwoods at home for pulp and profit and get your hardwood from the cheap labour of the endless tropics'* has been the motto for too long, a motto which has left a pretty sour feeling not only across the world but right in our own mis-managed back yard. Put factory firs and acid precipitation together, and the result is an ecological disaster. While the trees are singeing in the rain from too much acid and the absence of any lime to neutralize it, the life in the streams, rivers and lakes is killed off, and that includes fish like salmon and trout and birds like the dipper. It may seem very sensible to subsidize factory forestry and foul chimneys in the name of jobs created, but what about all the jobs lost at the other end of the landscape?

Acid landscapes are expensive problems. It has been estimated that Europe's agricultural and fishing industries are affected to the tune of over £200 million a year. In Scandinavia, acidity of the water supply has even been known to turn hair green: OK if you are going punk, unlucky if you are a Copenhagen maiden with lovely long streams of golden hair. The acidity in the water dissolves the copper in your supply pipes producing a green dye, and there you have, green hair.

Had enough of green hair, chemical explosions, coal heaps and carbon dioxide? You may ask what it would have been like in the good old days when there was no pollution and we burned only well-seasoned wood to warm ourselves and cook our food? To find out you don't have to go back in time, just take a trip to the present-day Third World.

If you still haven't finished your holiday in São Paolo get a guide and take a journey into the Brazilian interior, and have a look at how they cook the food in the villages.

Over two billion people in the undeveloped countries – that's almost half the human population – still depend on firewood as their primary energy source. Although it is a renewable resource, world supplies are being cut down faster than they are being replaced. Right at this point, at least 125 million people are unable to collect enough fire-wood for their needs, and that number grows daily.

In areas like the Indian and Nepal Himalayas, villagers exercising their traditional rights to collect wood, compete with the government's large-scale timber operations and independent logging firms exporting wood to the cities to provide for urban and industrial needs. There is acute scarcity all over the Third World. Collectively, they're cutting off the branch on which they live; and we are doing our bit too. Us? You may ask what have we got to do with it? The answer is in part staring you in the face, in your local shopping precinct and around your living room, perhaps even the chair you sit on or the bed you lie on: tropical hardwoods – smashing aren't they?

When Brendan Quayle was doing anthropological fieldwork in the sub-Himalayan mountain tracts of Kumaon's tiger country in the late seventies, wood shortages, not tigers, provided the greatest problem facing the villagers with whom he was living. Large tracts of once-forested hillsides lay bare and open to the sky. Tree growth was stunted by constant hacking at branches, and trunks were mutilated by the practice of cutting wounds in the trees to drain them for the resin needed in paraffin production. Everyday, parties of village women set out in the early hours for the oakwoods of the remoter tracts to collect wood, risking attacks by bears and bandits. After walks of twenty or thirty kilometres, taking many hours, they would return laden with great bundles on their heads. Each hard-won bundle part of a hardwood resource which would not be replaced in their lifetimes. The villagers always had a traditional right to forage for firewood; and there was no other fuel supply available in an area too hilly for cows and the dung commonly used as fuel in the Indian Plain villages.

But the real resource predators were the foresters. This was most apparent when the intrepid anthropologist had to use the mountain buses in the rainy season. Relays of buses had to be laid on, as every ten kilometres or so, stretches of entire roadside had collapsed or been covered in an avalanche of sliding mud and boulders, as soil from denuded, tree-less hillsides shifted to the valley bottoms. To get from bus to bus, passengers had to run for it across the mudslide, dodging flying boulders and the occasional tree trunk forgotten by the foresters. There were compensations. At the end of a journey, there was always the joy of hot curries and chapattis savouring and smelling of pine and oak charcoals. But what a price: the ecological structure of an entire area put at risk by the haphazard exploitation of its trees.

Wood may be relatively clean when burned as fuel, but the other environmental consequences are considerable. The deforestation of the Third World proceeds at an alarming pace. In the 20th century, India has eliminated over 80% of its traditional forest lands, China and Sri Lanka 90% and Brazil 40%. The results have been damning: soil erosion and soil deterioration, floods, sinking water tables, silted-up reservoirs, the expansion of deserts, and increased poverty for those who depend on the forest for fuels.

Uncooked food in hot countries is dangerous: cooking kills the parasites, bacteria and fungi. Fuel shortages encourage sickness and the spread of disease. On the Indian Plains, where villagers have had to turn to the use of animal dung as an alternative fuel supply, there is a cruel backlash. That dung would otherwise have been used to fertilize the land to grow much-needed food. In Asia and Africa alone, almost 400 million tonnes of dung are burned each year. If it was instead put on the fields, it could easily produce 20 million tonnes of grain – enough food to keep millions of people free from starvation every year.

Unless there is a substantial replanting of trees across the globe, wood as a world fuel is, like the dodo in *Alice in Wonderland*, heading for extinction. Well, you may ask, what primary organic or mineral energy source will then be left to fuel the world's future? If we can't rely on the great fuels of the past – wood, coal, gas or oil – to keep going, what about the 'fuel of the future'? You know, the one they told us when we were children was safe and clean, the answer to all our energy problems – nuclear power. They said it was going to be so cheap that we wouldn't need meters in our houses.

Nuclear energy is the area where the fuel crises really start to go critical. Electrical energy is generated through a controlled process of atomic fission which takes place inside a controlled environment called a 'reactor'. The nuclear or innermost parts of a uranium atom are placed in fuel rods and ruptured by neutrons which crash into them at speed, causing a chain reaction which generates great heat. This heat is transferred to pressurized water or gas which flows through a heat exchanger to heat other water and make steam. This turns a turbine, which in turn runs a generator, that produces electricity. Wonderful, tapping the power of the atom, effectively illustrating Einstein's theory of relativity, demonstrating the interchangeability of mass and energy. In a nuclear reaction, atomic mass is transferred through fission into energy.

But unfortunately, energy isn't the only thing that's produced. A by-product is radiation – highly dangerous particles and rays, which if released into the environment interfere with the vital structure of living things, directly causing lesions, cancers, and damage to reproductive systems which can lead to deformities in successive generations.

Very high doses of radiation are immediately fatal. The effect of very low doses only appears years after exposure and in humans cause a terrible wasting disease – leukaemia, cancer of the blood. The scientist Marie Curie and her daughter, well known for their work with the radio-active substance radium, which in low doses has great medical value, both died eventually from leukaemia. All radiation is dangerous, and it is widely agreed that there is no such thing as a truly 'safe' dose. The nuclear people do believe though that there are acceptable *levels* of exposure which, in their view are not concentrated enough to cause any cellular damage.

There is a variety of different kinds of nuclear reactors and processes, of which some have proved in history to be more unstable, or more prone to accidental releases of radio-activity, than others. Hence we have Advanced Gas-cooled Reactors (AGR's), High Temperature Gas-cooled Reactors (HTGR's), Light Water Reactors (LWR's) and Pressurized Water Reactors (PWR's) and so on. Mostly all are named after the type of process used to control or transfer the heat given off in the reactor. All of these reactors can leak, but only one can explode, the ominously-named fast-breeder reactor, which makes more efficient use of the uranium ore inside the reactor core, creating more fission and more energy. The fast-breeder brings together the most dangerous substance on earth – plutonium – with the most explosive, sodium.

The nuclear process also generates a number of other, highly radio-active elements including americium, iodine, tritium, caesium, strontium and krypton. But the most dangerous by-product of all is plutonium. This is a radio-active substance not found in nature and it is very dangerous, a bone-seeking poison. It takes over 24,000 years for only half its radio-activity to decay to a safe level (its 'half-life'); its toxic lifetime is more than a hundred times longer than all of recorded history. A minute quantity of plutonium ingested in the human body is a fatal dose; half a kilogram of plutonium equally distributed over the world has the potential to inflict cancer on every single peson. Yet each commercial reactor provides around 200 kilograms of the stuff every year. Not surprisingly, plutonium is also the core material used for making new nuclear bombs.

Nuclear reactors generate spent fuel which can be re-processed to recover unspent plutonium to start the whole thing off again . . . how convenient. But inconvenience and danger also come with the highly radio-active waste which remains. Almost everything that comes into contact with the reactor process or re-process becomes radio-active, including cooling water, equipment, dust, gloves, coats, pieces of machinery and so on. These all absorb radio-activity at varying intensities, high, medium and low, and are hazardous according to those intensities. They cannot be safely burned, unless you call radio-active smoke safe, so they have to be stored or disposed of – inevitably in the environment. All in all the nuclear process is a dangerous one. At the very start of the process is uranium mining. According to the UN, as many uranium miners die from lung cancer every year as coal miners killed in mining accidents. At the other end of the

process we can find some other very dangerous goings-on. Reactors intended for the production of nuclear power, for example, are used to produce the raw materials of nuclear weapons.

All industries have problems, but the nuclear industry has been plagued by leaks and accidents since its proliferation in the fifties and sixties. Few reactors have escaped unscathed, although details of leaks have often been suppressed by the industry. But the most disturbing incidents are well known: in 1957, a reactor at Windscale in Cumbria, UK, caught fire, contaminating an area of 2072 square kilometres around the plant; in 1958, a nuclear waste dump exploded in the Urals, USSR, creating a radio-active desert; in 1968, in Detroit, USA, a fast-breeder reactor core began to melt; in 1969 and 1972, in Colorado and New York there were explosions on work-sites containing plutonium; and in 1976 and 1981, at Windscale there were two further major leaks of radio-activity, one including a spill of 2 million litres of radio-active water. In a PWR at Three Mile Island in Harrisburg, USA in 1979, operator error led to the destruction of a $1 billion reactor and the release into the atmosphere of a huge

Sellafield, Cumbria, UK ... the world's first large-scale nuclear power station and one of the biggest single sources of radio-active pollution in the world.

cloud of radio-active gas. The whole plant was closed down and only re-opened six years later – after the radio-activity outside the doomed reactor was thought to have sufficiently decayed. Finally, in 1986 the fatal meltdown of a reactor at the Chernobyl, USSR plant had international implications, with radio-active material including plutonium carried by winds across Europe for months afterwards. Scientists have estimated that 50–100,000 people in the Ukraine were exposed to dangerous levels of radiation, and that up to 50,000 Europeans may contract cancer as a direct result of contamination by the Chernobyl cloud.

Nuclear power, like nuclear weaponry, has proliferated across the globe since the sixties. There are now more than 250 reactors in twenty-two countries. But these supply only 2% of the world's electricity, a poor return on the colossal sums spent on the technology involved. Most European countries and some communist-block countries have nuclear reactors, many of which regularly leak radio-activity into the atmosphere. There are also reactors in Third World countries with very unstable political and economic systems, with lax attitudes to public safety and environmental health. The list includes, Brazil, Argentina, Iran, Iraq, Pakistan, the Philippines and Libya.

The environmental record of the industry in India, the Third World country with the most ambitious nuclear programme, makes sober reading. India's Department of Atomic Energy is the most secretive nuclear establishment in the world, and it is free from all legal and economic constraints, answerable to no public legislature or auditor. The nuclear programme consists of five reactors, with three more under construction and built entirely with Indian expertise and technology. The first two reactors at Tarakpur, Bombay, both went critical in 1969, and two others in Rajasthan went critical in 1973 and 1982 respectively. A reactor at Narora in Uttar Pradesh is sited close to the line of the Moradabad Fault, the site of a severe earthquake in 1956, and near to the Ganges, which floods during every other monsoon season.

The designs have been subject to constant modifications; few have attained more than 50% operating capacity; and there is a high turnover in the workforce. A visitor to one reactor described seeing workers perched on high rafters on the reactor plant operating the radio-active wastes with long bamboo poles, and radio-active water was observed gushing from the reactor core through a tube to the environment outside. Worker and public safety standards and provisions are nil to non-existent: villagers who know nothing of the dangers of radiation are employed casually to clean up after accidents, and given bonuses after they have received large radiation doses. No medical records are kept, so no local deaths can be traced to the plants.

Nuclear Madness, you may say, and all for less than 2½% of India's electricity supply needs. But despite everything, the programme is set to expand, with the industry's main critics effectively silenced. Its record so far taken into account India's nuclear industry seems indeed set for its first Bhophal: it can only be a matter of time.

One of the curiosities of Third World reactors is the names they are given, usually the names of underworld deities or biblical tribes, regarded with awe and

India's atomic reactor at Trombay is modelled in the image of Siva, the Hindu god of Creation ... and Destruction.

fear. India took this process of conferring cosmic authenticity on nuclear reaction one step further by modelling the design of its reactor at Trombay, on the iconic sexual image of the Hindu god Siva, the 'Destroyer'.

The potential for the destruction of human life and the environment contained in nuclear power generation across the globe is immense, through accidents, leaks, seismic tremors, poor design or terrorist attack. With so many reactors worldwide there would, in fact, be no need for atomic weapons in certain theatres of potential war: a few conventional missiles targeted in the right places would do the same job. The destruction already associated with nuclear weapon production and testing and the waste they accumulate is terrifying. According to the cancer research scientist Dr Rosalie Bertell:

> 'The global victims of the radiation pollution related to nuclear weapon production, testing, use and waste conservatively, number 13 million. The current rate of weapon production globally (1985) generates between 7000 and 15,000 victims yearly (between 20 and 40 a day) even without further nuclear weapon testing.'[7]

The age of atomic destruction is not just a thing of the future: it is already upon us.

Back in Europe it is nuclear waste that worries most people. Twenty-seven years after the first commercial nuclear reactor began operating, no-one has found a way of dealing with radio-active waste, particularly the long-term stuff like plutonium. In the United Kingdom alone, it was admitted by the Department of the Environment in 1985, that by the year 2000 AD, the country will have accumulated over one million tonnes of low-level nuclear waste, more than 160,000 tonnes of intermediate waste dangerous for 50,000 years, and more than 4000 tonnes of high-level waste toxic for 250,000 years. All this is waste for which there is as yet no home. It is largely the product of nuclear power generation, and is accumulating in silos and ponds around the plants that create it.

To deal with this problem the UK's waste management agency, Nirex, has been investigating sites where they can build huge underground mausoleums in which to dump the stuff. But as no-one wants nuclear waste in or under their own backyard, they are being pushed from pillar to post; at each post they are faced by a public inquiry at which concerned local citizens air their doubts about not just nuclear waste, but the nuclear industry itself. Indeed an opinion poll conducted by the magazine *New Scientist* in 1985 showed that, of those interviewed, a clear majority was more frightened by the dangers of nuclear energy than any other scientific or technological process. To most people it is incredible that the UK has no acceptable policy or available technology for disposing safely of nuclear wastes, either on land or at sea. Yet successive governments have been committed to a continual expansion of the nuclear industry. This in turn has led to an even greater accumulation of wastes well beyond their mandate.

The international nuclear lobby is a colossal empire, an industrial and military complex which operates in great secrecy, often with its own security forces, its nuclear police. Nuclear powers trade with one another, in technology, spent fuel, raw materials and even plutonium, and this is a trade which recognizes no enemies. It has long been thought that the US provides the USSR with plutonium for warheads which, in the event of a war, could be used against the USA itself. In 1984, the grounding of a large cargo ship in the English Channel, the *Mont Louis*, exposed the French transporting canisters of a radio-active gas, uranium hexafluoride, to a port in Russia. It is little wonder then that with so much trade at stake, the same administration feared the *Rainbow Warrior*.

On the continued existence and expansion of the nuclear industry depend the careers and salaries of large numbers of scientists, researchers and technicians. If the industry goes under on environmental grounds and public pressure, there is a lot to lose: and this explains to an extent the occasional acts of sabotage and murder which have been committed against anti-nuclear activists. However, the nuclear industry is in trouble in the 1980s, not simply environmentally but also economically. In both America and Europe, many new nuclear installations are years behind schedule and are costing five to ten times the original projections. In America, plans for 100 new plants have been shelved and no new plants have been ordered since 1977. The market place there does not see nuclear installations as cost-effective: so there are no plans for new reprocessing or fuel-enrichment plants which would allow the industry to try out new technology. European countries on the other hand, support the drive towards the construction of new reprocessing plants, despite a current world glut in uranium and falling ore prices, because the nuclear industry is a public utility which commands a large public investment in research and development.

At the end of the day it is hard to establish whether the nuclear industry is at all cost-effective. We don't as yet know the true costs of cleaning up the fuel cycle and disposing of the wastes that result. In 1978, the US House of Representatives stated that:

> 'When the still unknown costs of radio-active waste and spent fuel management, decommissioning and perpetual care are finally included in the base rate, nuclear power might prove to be much more expensive than conventional energy alternatives, such as coal.'

If we take into account the heavy subsidies and energy costs absorbed in uranium processing, in production, reactor construction, research and the transport of waste, the economic logic of the enterprise in the long term seems even less clear. Nuclear power, in addition to losing radio-activity on a daily basis, also appears to be losing money.

Environmentally the nuclear industry, both power and weaponry, provides possibly the greatest threat to our planet's well-being and the survival of the human species. Is it right that we should be trading in poisons which can survive up to a quarter of a million years? And how do we secure radio-active plant, reactor core and spent fuel from contact with the environment for periods extending well beyond our own lifetimes? Is it right that we should consign our children and grandchildren to the risk of future radiation poisoning, to live their lives on the edge of darkness?

RECHARGING THE FUTURE

If you are still with us by that swimming pool in São Paolo and that welter of depressing facts and figures didn't drive you to the pool bar, then you deserve a good cheering up, and a good cooling off to get rid of the acid taste in your throat. Come with us in an ethanol-powered cab to the beach at Santos. It's time to go windsurfing.

That's the life. Within minutes we're in the middle of the bay, free as birds, going maybe 40 or 50 mph. The power is incredible – and it's all natural: energy from the sun, the wind, the waves and the tide. Perhaps these are the areas we've got to look to for the fuel of the future?

Let's start with the sun, the source of all energy, and the greatest nuclear reactor of them all. Research into trapping the heat energy of the sun and converting that into electrical power has been conducted in Europe since the last century. But the investment so far is small, and the successes in research and development have been correspondingly small. Various techniques have been deployed: great reflecting mirrors placed in the landscape which beam rays from the sun into a collecting tower which carries hot molten salt to a generator; solar ponds which absorb the sun's heat in salt water, linked to a turbine which is driven by the temperature difference between the hot and cold water in the pond; converting solar energy directly to electricity using photo-electric cells — just like the light meter in your camera. These are all highly effective, if expensive systems, but it is difficult to store the energy that is trapped; and in those parts of the world where energy consumption is greatest, the sun unfortunately doesn't always shine.

But it has been shining on a couple of model schemes: two of the biggest in Europe, at Adrano in Sicily and Almeria in Spain, each supply 500 kilowatts to their national grids every year. Another successful station at Barstow in California, US, has a peak output of 12,000 kilowatts every year: enough to fry a year's supply of eggs. Although these are all done with mirrors, they're no trick, but the beginning of something big.

Solar energy can also be used in a small way to add energy efficiency to our

Tapping some of the sun's free energy at an experimental solar power plant in the USA.

houses, through the use of glass panels on walls and roofs, double-glazing and double walls which use sheets of glass to heat up inside walls – another dimension of the greenhouse effect. This 'passive' solar heating could cut swathes into our fuel bills, contributing to over 40% of our domestic hot water needs in one year. But the design features involved have yet to become standard housing practice – partly because of a lack of committment in official and business quarters. The excuse often given to the consumer is that 'it's all sunshine, Sunshine.' But the reality is that in the market place, the very renewability of solar power is its worst enemy. Value is attributed to things that are scarce or at least limited, like oil and coal, but not to things which are plentiful and ultimately free, like sunshine. Traditionally, the prospect of heating systems controlled locally by consumers does not appeal to the energy lobby, which wants us to spend and consume, not use and renew.

With the price of photo-electric cells and reflective materials falling tenfold, it has been estimated that solar electricity costs could compete with fossil and nuclear fuel costs by the end of the century. Our task is to hurry that along. There are no obvious environmental side effects, no pollution or radiation, except in the case of one dotty scheme involving solar-collecting panels in space beaming energy microwaves to locations on earth. Fortunately this would be too costly and dangerous to implement. But in general the case for solar power is a good one. We just need the energy officials to take the clouds out of their heads and think about the future.

Sunny side up then, and if you're not feeling too sunburned, how about the wind. There's no shortage of wind supplies in the world, offshore and inland, and we've had windmill technology for more than 2000 years, driving water pumps and turning millstones.

Windsurfing apart, catching the wind, like trapping the sun, can be a complicated process, but although official commitment is low, the potential for providing future energy supplies is enormous. Modern schemes involve rotary blades and metal towers rather than sails and old friendly looking mills, but they are much more energy-efficient. There are now some eighty-odd wind farms in California, creating surreal landscapes of whirring rotary blades, and generating as much electricity as 350,000 barrels of oil a year. Indeed the California Energy Commission has set a modest target whereby the state wind farms are expected to catch enough wind by the year 2000 to provide over 10% of the state's energy demand. This is more than it could possibly achieve through nuclear power, and it's a very demanding state.

The masters of wind power are the Danish who have over one thousand large wind turbines dotted around their country supplying electricity to their national grid; and exporting machines and expertise to the rest of the world. The UK is just beginning to catch on and two large projects are now under way. One involves the construction of a 60-metre diameter horizontal-axis machine on the wind-blown Orkney islands, and the other involves the construction of a novel, 25-metre vertical axis machine at Carmarthen Bay in Wales. The possibilities are endless: offshore island wind banks, wind turbines out at sea; wind machines on isolated hill tops and in areas of industrial dereliction. The environmental impact is minimal: noise levels can be controlled and, if like the Danes you don't mind the sight of modern wind-mills, the visual impact would be considerably less than that of conventional coal or nuclear installations.

There is even a growing market for wind technology in the Third World. An alternative energy group from Hexham in England has for years been successfully exporting portable wind turbines to the Nomads of Outer Mongolia. The Nomads move constantly over wind-swept, fuel-less plateaux with their flocks, and these mini-windmills allow them to stop the march at any point for a quick cup of tea! Wind is in fact a highly practical way of supplying the energy needs of those developing countries where population is scattered and communications are poor. Wind turbines can also be used to lift water for irrigation. In general these are more environmentally and economically appropriate in the rural agricultural areas than the huge multi-purpose power plants which these countries are being encouraged to buy from western engineering consortiums.

Like energy from the sun, energy from the wind receives a very low level of investment in research and development from the UK, yet British technology in this area is as sophisticated as Denmark's, and can benefit from proportionally higher coastal and offshore windspeeds — 7–8 metres a second, as compared to the Danes 5–6 metres a second. Again, of course, a major obstacle is the unease of the traditional energy sector: they cannot plan for growth with resources that are naturally renewable and as the ultimate oil crisis is not here yet, there's not much pressure on them to make the appropriate investment. The winds of change have yet to come, but change is inevitable. And if you have managed to stay on that windsurfer's sailboard, or ever stood on an Orkney foreshore in a Force 10 gale — or ever, for that matter, sat in the visitor's gallery in Britain's House of Commons, then you will realize that there's plenty of wind — and it's not *all* just hot air.

So how about wave and tide power? It's not all just fresh air and moonshine; there's no shortage of energy out there at sea to drive some turbines; there are great resources of power and motion. In fact there have been tidal mills since 1233, when the Priory of the Holy Trinity at Aldgate in London used the tides to grind their flour. The incoming tide flowed into a millpond. At high water its gates were closed. And after the tide had ebbed the gates were opened, the water flowed out and drove the mill. Brilliant but simple. The trouble was they could never maintain a consistent output of power because of the constant variation in the tide throughout the year. The same problem besets modern tidal installations like the one at Rance in France, which can produce up to 240,000 kilowatts.

The variability of weather conditions at sea presents similar problems to any programme of generating energy from the waves. Various types of technology have been proposed including; bobbing tanks on the surface of the sea which drive high pressure water pumps, and batteries of floating vanes fitted with pistons and pumps that are driven by the movement of the waves. The potential for wave power in the UK has been estimated at 6000 megawatts a year from a range of technological applications. This is considerable: it represents over 12% of

Left *The world's largest wind generator, Washington, USA.*

Below *Blowin' in the wind ... cows graze beneath the latest wind turbine generators – that make a relevant contribution to California's energy demands.*

Britain's electricity-generating capacity, and one-and-a-half times our present nuclear capacity.

But there has been a lot of ebbing and flowing about wave power from the politicians and developers. In 1985, despite the predicted gains from wave energy, the UK government decided to discontinue its modest investment in wave energy research and development. A few months later the Norwegians opened a wave power station at Bergen. This used largely British technology, cost only half a million pounds to build and is expected to produce more energy at a cheaper rate than the newest, most efficient coal-fired plant. The device is called— wait for it — A Multi-resonant Oscillating Water Column, and consists of a 60-foot chimney standing against the rocks in deep water. As the waves rise and fall, air is compressed and used to drive a turbine.

If the Norwegian experiment proves successful, this could easily be emulated across the globe; as could the principle of laying down barrages in estuaries to capture the power of the tides. In Britain alone there are a number of uniquely suitable sites: including the Severn and the Mersey. The Severn Estuary has a tidal range of 12 metres and clearly represents one of the best opportunities in the world to harness tidal power for electricity generation.

In addition to technologies which trap the power of Sun, Wind, Wave and Tide, there are many other methods for extricating energy from the natural forces of the earth and its biosphere: a long list includes geothermal aquifers, ocean thermal energy conversion, geothermal hot dry rocks, and 'run of river' hydro-electric power, a type of HEP which does not involve constructing huge dams. All of these, like sun, wind, wave and tide, are essentially non-polluting and will

The awesome power of the sea just waiting to be tapped as a colossal future energy source.

have minimal impact on the environment. But they will require further research and technological development before they escape the shadows of the laboratory or the test site and are brought out into the pure white light of power production. However the fact that these processes exist, are being developed and have power-producing possibilities, is encouraging – an indication that the tide is beginning to turn, at least in the favour of renewable natural energy resources.

On that note of hope it's time for us to get off our sailboards and back to Britain to see what else has been happening on the alternative energy front while we've been away.

WEALTH GOING TO WASTE

Back home in chilly Britain, we're in search straightaway for a little bit of sunshine. One place where that's pretty well guaranteed, despite the fact that its a very rainy place, is at the Centre for Alternative Technology (CAT) at Machynlleth in Wales. Set up in 1974 as both an energy park and a working village, the residents are experimenting with new ways of producing energy and with new more efficient ways of using the energy we already have.

Concerned with the high levels of resource and energy consumption current in the Western World today, and seeking to encourage an awareness of our true place in the environment, the CAT people have built working systems of windmills, waterwheels, solar power and biogas production units. Every house is well insulated, and every building incorporates energy-saving additions and water-saving devices. They do all their own engineering and grow a lot of their own food – using the waste to create energy.

It's all a bit back-to-naturish in one way, but in every other way it's highly scientific and sensible. There's a feeling here of actually living as nature intended: comfortably, organically and in a state of ecological equilibrium with your surroundings. You can really relax in a bath here, even if it is in a geodesic dome, knowing that the energy is not being wasted. If these people had their way, not only bathtime, but our entire lifestyles would be powered by the sun, the winds, and the waters: all good clean stuff, and thanks to nature, it will never run out. No-one is saying that if every house had its own windmill then we'd have no energy problems. The point is that there *are* ways of making energy which don't rely on coal, or oil or uranium, and perhaps a combination of these could provide many of the answers.

Machynlleth is independent of direct government funding and exists on its extensive visitor appeal and what is manufactured there for sale. It is 80% reliant on renewable resources for its energy needs, and the other 20% is accounted for by the extra needs involved in providing for the visitors at peak times. The place works on a shoe-string – imagine what they could do with the kind of government investment and political backing which is given to the country's nonrenewable energy programmes, particularly nuclear power. This is despite the fact that these giant programmes are wasteful, form a blot on the landscape, cause huge amounts of pollution and will eventually run out. And we accept it. Yet things don't have to be like this . . . in some other parts of the world, and even in parts of Britain, they've already begun to realize that there is another way, and it works.

Back up home in the north-east of England there are examples of industries and factories which have made huge savings in energy, simply by investing a little thought and money into the problem. One unlikely example is the Spartan-Redheugh Steel Plate Mill in what was once the centre of steel making in Britain. It was built six years ago, one of the last rolling mills to be constructed in Europe, shades of prosperity past. It's a powerhouse of heat and noise, molten metal and roaring furnaces, sparks and steam flying everywhere. Lots of energy and, you would think, much of it going to waste. But no, they've installed energy-saving furnaces here and found they could cut gas consumption by more than half.

This company has survived the closures not only because it has increased its steel output, but it has reduced the amount of energy that's needed to turn steel slabs into plate. The furnace is so well designed that the heat no longer goes up the chimney, it goes into the steel, and practically nowhere else. As a result, the firm won an award for its energy-saving ideas, and deserves another for producing without polluting. It's sound economy too – the firm's doing better business in an industry that's been going to the dogs for years.

The message from this backyard of the north-east is clear enough: conservation pays. In recent years that message has been echoing across the globe. In America, the Tennessee Valley Authority established by Roosevelt in the early days of energy development as part of the New Deal, now treats conservation as a resource – not just as a saving, but as a power supply option. How can that be? You may well ask, but the TVA argues that energy conservation has a better payback record, shorter lead times, greater flexibility and certainty than the alternatives. They believe that new conservation programmes will add 3000 to 4000 megawatts to their overall capacity. Another American public utility, the Bonneville Power Administration, has demonstrated that its most cost-effective resource is conservation. The message is loud and clear here too: consider conservation as an alternative energy supply, cost it, invest in it, and you end up making money. It's not a question of cutting back, it's a question of making more effective use of what you've already got.

The trouble is, too many of our politicians, scientists and developers aren't getting the message. They're too ready to squander more money and more energy on new plant, new nuclear power stations and new energy exploration. More and more megaschemes doesn't necessarily mean more and more megawatts: look at Britain's new generation of nuclear power stations, like Hartlepool in Tees-side, some of them ten years behind schedule, ten times the original estimated cost, and after ten years still nowhere near their intended output. Yet they are planning to build another one up the coast from Hartlepool, on the edge of a great coalfield.

However, nor far away there is a bright spot on the horizon: the firm of Thorn EMI in County Durham. This firm makes energy-consuming appliances, from refrigerators to ovens, but it deploys energy-saving techniques all the way down the production line, and even better, recycles all its waste products, making fuel

Opposite
The Centre for Alternative Technology at Machynlleth, Wales experiments with new renewable ways of producing energy – like this aero-generator and energy-conserving house.

Drying cow-pats for fuel in India ... a bit basic, perhaps – but there are more socially-acceptable sources and methods for creating such safe and efficient bio-fuel.

from the rubbish. For this company there's no such thing as rubbish: it's all energy, true mass into energy, highly Einsteinian.

Now there's an energy source with potential – if you think of all the rubbish we produce in our factories and homes every single day: energy by the binful, and yet we mostly bury it in the ground, spending vast amounts of money and energy carting it to the tip. But there are exceptions: in the West Midlands, work has just begun on the UK's first commercial-scale, refuse-derived fuel plant to turn 100,000 tons a year of industrial and household rubbish into 30,000 tons of fuel. The rubbish is chopped up and compressed into pellets which are sold just like coal for burning. In energy terms, two buckets of pellets equals one bucket of coal. It's hardly rubbish – it's making money as well as energy, a potential pollutant is eliminated from the environment, and there are other environmental advantages: refuse-derived fuel gives off less than 10% of the sulphur emissions that coal produces. Where there's muck there's brass – and apparently the UK produces enough combustible 'muck' every year, enough glowing heat, to match 10% of all the coal consumed in the country.

Coal too has a valuable rubbish component – all the wasted heat and gas which escapes through our chimneys and cooling towers every year. But this too can be harnessed, through a process known as CHP or 'Combined Heat and Power'. All that's required is altering the design and mode of our coal-fired power stations so that the excess heat is converted into hot water that can be used to provide district heating schemes for tens of thousands of urban households.

Experiments on combined heat and power, and related district heating schemes, have proved these to be a highly successful way of getting more energy for our money. If the appropriate investment was committed to the necessary development of these schemes, another burning problem would be resolved: the problem of unemployment. It has been estimated that CPH has the potential to provide almost half a million years of direct employment in construction, the power to generate 400,000 new jobs. Clearly, if these schemes are not brought into being, a lot of heat and a lot of jobs will be frozen out, but also our fossil fuels resources will be depleted quicker, and both we and our environment will be losers.

To bring the whole energy question right back into our own homes and backyards there's a lot we can do here to improve our own energy efficiency. Thermal blocks can be built into new homes, from the foundations up; wall cavities can be filled with insulating materials; roofs and pipes can be lagged to keep the heat in; draughts can be driven out and hot air can be trapped in; using double-glazing and computer sensing. Making our homes energy-efficient saves money for the householder and energy for the world, and it could provide a plethora of job opportunities.

But one of the most promising sources of alternative energy in the world today can be found in the very heart of our more traditional homes – by the fireside. In the days before coal this was where we used to burn nature's first fuel – wood. Clearly though, it would not make economic or environmental sense for us all to turn back to the wood fire, or instal wood burning stoves in every household. But if we used wood as a modern bio-fuel, by converting wood wastes along with other organic residues, like bracken and other quick growing vegetable matter, into bio-gas, alcohol or charcoal, we would have a regularly renewable energy source. With this in mind, Canada's energy department has calculated that its annual sources of wood-waste can be processed into between 50–70 million tonnes of fuel alcohol every year. Equally in the US, it has been calculated that if American bio-mass resources were more intensively managed, they could supply up to 20% of their total energy demand. Bio-mass, now there's a good word with a hi-tech tinge; planted in the right places with other terms like Short Rotation Forestry, we can see these as the key buzzwords in an all-new, all-systems-grow, bio-technological revolution.

Bio-mass already fuelled an early part of one revolution, the Industrial Revolution before the transition to coal; then they burned wood and still had enough left

Harvesting energy from trees. A significant revival of the ancient arts of woodland management and coppicing could provide an important renewable energy source.

over to make ships for more voyages of discovery. They had a renewable supply too, pure bio-technology, in the shape of coppice woodland. Woodlots were harvested at intervals of five to twenty-two years and allowed to grow again. The result was a continued cover of mixed broadleaf woodland which protected the soil from leaching and erosion and provided it with an annual supply of humus, Nature's free fertilizer. The coppice tradition protected and promoted a vast array of wildflowers, birds and animals and produced a lot of wood of different sizes including standard full-grown trees, thirty to a hectare. With all these benefits — how come we let it go?

Coppice could, however, have its second spring. New research has shown that if 100,000 hectares were planted and managed as coppice, this would keep a 500 megawatt power station supplied with all its energy needs and ensure a supply of not less than 40,000 mature tree trunks per annum.

If bio-mass could happen in the cooler, short-growing season climates of Britain and the USA, just think of the potential in the tropical rain forests of South America and South East Asia. As we write this chapter, no less than 30 hectares of such forest are being clear-felled every minute, and at a very maximum only 2–5 hectares are being replanted: that's a net loss of more than 1400 hectares of tropical hardwoods every day. It's a veritable slaughter of a potentially huge reservoir of bio-mass energy, notwithstanding the loss of wildlife habitats and the destruction of the livelihoods of local forest tribes.

If, on the other hand, we were able to replace this quick-grab insanity with some form of coppice cropping and whole-system forestry, then the vast majority of those negatives become positives. Local wildlife would still have a home, the local people would have jobs within an indigenous forest landscape, and even the scorch-earth timber companies could look forward to growing profits in the future. The potential is enormous. If only 10% of the tropical rainforest were replanted and managed in this way, it could fuel the world's power supply to the tune of 30 million megawatts, and that's based on very conservative estimates. If we called it coppice it would be depreciated by the critics as a kind of green medieval madness. If we called it 'whole system bio-technology' it could indeed happen. In any case, there's nothing in a name, but there's lots of power in the trees. We just have to see beyond the wood.

But are our leaders, with all the facts at their disposal, making the right decisions for us and our environment? Is it right that, in the UK for example, the government's centre for research into renewable energy is based at its central nuclear establishment at Harwell, the very same establishment which once objected that wave energy frightens fish! Is it right that in the 1980s the budget for research and development into renewables stands at only £14 million per year, while the budget into research and development for the nuclear industry currently gobbles up at least thirteen times that amount? Is it right that governments pretend to have a fuel policy based on diversity of all energy resources, when in fact over 95% of all the eggs are put in two baskets – nuclear power and fossil fuels – rather than into the multitude of baskets which exist, including those provided by conservation and the renewables?

If British industry saved half the energy we know it could, we would need thirteen less fossil fuel or nuclear power stations. If British households saved half the energy we know they could, we would need another nine fewer power stations. If we used only half our rubbish for the generation of electricity, another six fewer stations would be needed. That means, in pure energy terms, almost a quarter of our existing stations are draining our fossil fuel reserves unnecessarily and blotting our landscapes and our lives without justification.

If we wanted to follow Europe and the rest of the thinking world and cut down our emissions of sulphur dioxide by 30%, cutting our capacity for new-energy production would be one very tangible way of doing it. But a programme of power station closures would probably be politically unacceptable even in a case of surplus energy production. 'What about the jobs?', the politicians and unions would say. But if we could clean the power stations up and resisted the temptation to build new ones, the power saved would in fact be used to create new jobs. The fact of the matter is that we can create two-and-a-half times more jobs for every unit of energy saved than for every new unit generated through building more and more nuclear power stations. Of course there isn't the same hi-tech glamour in double-glazing or cavity-wall insulation as there is in 'atomic core corrosion abatement' but if we changed the emphasis to energy servicing and away from environmental sacrifice, everybody's needs would be better served.

The deposit account of world energy is being overdrawn, taking us and our environment into the red. We're burning up our current stocks at a horrendous rate. The time has come to put both balances in order before the energy bank goes bust.

3 FEEDING THE WORLD

STOCKING UP FOR THE FUTURE

A guided tour of the global food garden reveals that it is stocked with iniquities. The economies of the rich north groan with the weight of indisposable food mountains. Yet an avalanche of foodstuffs pours out of the poor south into northern markets, out of the hands and away from the mouths of those who need the food most. The environment suffers too. The pressure of intensive agricultural production puts immense strain on soil, water resources and wildlife.

Ravaged by desertification, erosion, soil exhaustion and chemical pollution, parts of the global garden, north and south, are fit to burst. The tragedies of the Sahel and of Ethiopia could be just the first major cracks.

We go back in time to look at the story of Farmer Giles and to evaluate some of the social and ecological costs of the agricultural 'progress' in both the First and the Third Worlds. And we examine the potential of a new kind of green revolution both to feed the world and provide a place for wildlife.

Is it right that we allow the global garden to decay any further, held together by chemical fixes and 'band aid'? What hope is there of truly green growth and food for all?

TWO GARDENS

To see how we feed ourselves we'll take a visit to two gardens lying side by side. Approaching from the distance, we can see that one looks a little bit like a transplant from wildwood, a mass of tangled foliage, while the other looks more like a supermarket shelf, with everything neatly arranged in rows.

Up close there doesn't seem to be a lot of difference, apart from a pile of differently-coloured drums at the end of one garden and two piles of rotting compost in the other. The rain falls and the sun shines equally on both, but there are significant differences between the two: the wilder garden is managed organically, using natural resources to create its fertility, while the more orderly garden is managed using 'modern' methods, with mechanical aids and chemicals. Both are equally productive, but there are some essential differences. There are two different gardeners too. They're friendly enough but don't see eye to eye on the subject of garden management. Occasionally they can be heard over the garden fence:

GEORGE: There you go again, wasting energy turning that smelly compost heap, why don't you stop playing at gardening.

PAUL: I'm not playing around with anyone else's energy or with anyone else's environment. Most of the energy that goes into this garden is my own.

GEORGE: And look at all those flies and worms – pests I call them. Why don't you borrow my backpack spray and get some real hi-tech garden sense? Have some fertilizer as well, that'll speed things up for you.

PAUL: No way! I've got my compost heaps, they're the heart of my organic system – they're alive like the soil. The only chemicals I might use are based on natural products which break down rapidly in the soil. Here, have a few worms to put some organic life back into your garden.

GEORGE: No thanks, I do things the modern way. I get my garden done in a fraction of the time it takes you – then I've time to go jogging. And besides, just think of all those people I keep employed providing me with chemical and mechanical aids.

PAUL: Well I keep healthy the organic way; my soft garden technology works. It provides me and my family with good wholesome food and keeps me fit into the bargain; I don't need to go jogging. And there are wider issues at stake.

For me it's just a hobby. But for two thirds of the world it's a life-support system: they produce the vast bulk of their foods without using all these modern aids, but with the sweat of their backs, their own muscle power.

The other third, our third, do it your way. It may be modern and scientific, but it means we use up two thirds of the earth's resources, all the chemicals and the energy – to produce food we can't use!

GEORGE: Well, at least our way means that we're not starving, or crawling about scratching a living dependent on handouts.

PAUL: But we're doing well at the expense of the world's natural resources, most of which come from desperately poor countries in which people live constantly under the threat of malnutrition. It's a good thing all the Third World doesn't behave like you. We'd soon run out of resources.

GEORGE: Stark, staring nonsense. They're just inefficient. The only way to get the Third World out of their poverty trap is for them to adopt our scientific methods. It helps them, and it keeps our industries going – just think of all the chemicals, tractors and fertilizers they will need. Your organic way hasn't helped them so far has it. All they've got to do is adopt our system and their problems are solved.

By the way, have some of my tomatoes, I've got more than I need, I'd only have to chuck them away otherwise.

PAUL: There you go again – you've over-produced. If I took the easy way out and said yes thanks every year, I'd soon lose any incentive to grow my own. Anyway I prefer my own. I know exactly what's gone on 'em and in 'em, all the minerals came from the compost via the soil and the energy from the sun and me. Your tomatoes need more than 300 times as much energy and most of it is fossil fuel, the equivalent of 2 litres of petrol for every pampered pound.

GEORGE: That's not very grateful! Here, I'll mush them up and you can put them
on your compost heap.

PAUL: OK. Thanks I'll wash 'em first. Tell you what, I'll buy you a drink in
return. Even better, I'll give you a race to the pub and we'll see who's the
fitter.

Two gardens, two gardeners, two different ways of producing food; but we don't
know until the end of the race which way is the best, either for the health of the
two gardeners or of the global garden itself.

GROWING PAINS

One place where we can go to sample the fruits of the global garden is our local
wholefood shop. Here you can savour the smells and tastes and colours of products
from the whole of this earth: long grain rice from South East Asia; brazils from
South America; cardamoms, peppercorns, chillis, liquorice roots, seeds and
spices. It's an international larder, and all good healthy stuff.

The trouble is, many of these products have been produced in Third World
countries where people are dying with conditions related to malnutrition. And
increasingly, the production processes haven't been that healthy. The First
World has become extremely successful in foisting production techniques on to
the Third World, that may be quite unsuited to the different climates, soils,
conditions and cultures. They are invariably inadequately tested over the long-

*Seeds, spices ... and recycled
wrapping paper in an Indian
market.*

term and their environmental record in the short-term is abysmal. You've heard the one about the dust bowls of America, well hear now the story of Farmer Giles, or a Parable of British Agriculture.

Britain's First Agricultural Revolution is thought to have taken place around 3800 BC and was led by one of history's great revolutionaries, Neolithic Man. He discovered that the same piece of land could grow crops more than once if it was left to rest between periods of cultivation. He laid down the foundations of fallow. A Second Agricultural Revolution took place between 1750 and 1850. Britain's open countryside was divided up by the landowners into a network of smaller field units ringed by stone walls, hedges, fences and roads. Fallow figured prominently in the patchwork system of fields and field uses which resulted.

In subsequent years, Farmer Giles discovered how to bypass poor old fallow, initially by rotating different crops which were meant to complement each other in what they took from and put back into the soil. Then science identified the key nutrients in the soil which spurred crop growth. It turned out that one of the world's richest resources of these nutrients was guano – bird droppings. So in the early days of the revolution great fleets of sailing ships headed for the guano islands off the coast of Peru to bring home to the soils of Europe vast quantities of guano goodness. However, the world and Farmer Giles soon ran short and turned to the mining of rock nitrates, phosphate and potash, and then to great agro-chemical complexes which fixed nitrogen from the atmosphere. Guano, as a resource of good husbandry, like fallow, was rendered obsolete by the white-hot

Gifts from a balanced global garden in a Balinese vegetable market.

Before the days of
mono-cropping and pesticides
there was room for man,
animals and wildlife to live in
relative harmony.

heat and rapid growth of chemical technology. Unlike guano, however, fallow may be due for a comeback.

Agriculture and rural life in Britain, the land of Farmer Giles, had been on a slippery downslope since the Industrial Revolution. Thanks to the 'slave' labour of the Empire and the colonies, food could be imported more cheaply than it could be grown. Large areas of fertile land were lying in disuse. Our rural communities suffered appalling dereliction and rural poverty stalked the land. Then came the war; and a sudden upsurge in demand for extra domestic food supplies. These sustained the war effort and filled the yawning gap created by the severing of cheap imports from America and Russia and elsewhere. The government offered the earth to increase inputs and Farmer Giles could suddenly get better prices for his produce.

By the end of the war, like everyone else he was still producing like mad. But the agricultural supports were removed and this led to a total collapse in prices. So poor old Farmer Giles was suddenly burdened with surplus capacity and a collapsed market. Embittered by broken government promises he retreated into a new rural wilderness. One observer of the rural scene saw everywhere –

> 'Buildings in a deplorable state, roofs defective, doors broken down and the walls affording but little shelter. The farm roads are neglected and the farmyards in wet weather are deep in slush and liquid manure; the gates are broken down, or patched up anyhow, and the fields often enough, with their wastes of weeds and rubbish, cry aloud for land drainage.'[8]

Then came the Second World War. Farmer Giles was once again exhorted to achieve maximum productivity. He responded to a new range of incentives by doubling his output. This continued even after the end of the war because post-war fuel shortages still held food prices up. And after a couple of years he was rewarded for his war effort with the *Agriculture Act* of 1947, aimed at increasing Britain's capacity for self-sufficiency in food and improving the lot of Farmer Giles. By its clauses, Farmer Giles was guaranteed good prices for his produce in the market place. He was offered subsidies for improvements, to raise production levels and was given his own government-funded, professional advice service. Farmer Giles was now smiling, and deservedly so, for his efforts had effectively fed Britain through two World Wars.

Over the following two decades, the supports and subsidies to agriculture were sustained. So that by the 1970s, Farmer Giles' income had tripled: he was no longer smiling, he was laughing – for the moment at least – all the way to the bank. His bank manager, keen to lend vast sums in this thriving, government-backed business was laughing even louder. So too were the agro-chemical industries upon whose products high levels of agricultural production were now well and truly fixed. The mutual glee of Bank Manager, Farmer and our Agro-Industrialist reached a crescendo when Britain joined the Common Market. Because under the policy of the European Economic Community, Farmer Giles became eligible for extra measures of price protection, more improvement subsidies and capital grants and was offered guaranteed markets in Europe. Any surplus food for which there was no market either at home or abroad would be bought by the member governments and put into 'intervention stores' ready for a rainy day.

The CAP or Common Agricultural Policy of the European Community thus set the seed for growing food surpluses. It also turned Farmer Giles into a comparatively fatter, wealthier, merrier man. On the farm the revolution brought a massive transformation. Out went horses, haycarts and horse-troughs, and, worst of all, many of the hired hands, the ploughmen, stockmen, dairy girls and half the farmers themselves. In came tractors, combines, bailers, spray systems, fertilizers, pesticides, intensive farming methods. And as capital replaced labour, so too the countryside began to take on a machine-made rather than man-made appearance, with large field systems, farm amalgamations and neatly trimmed, regulated field and farm boundaries. We ploughed the fields and battered the goodness from the land.

'You can't make an omelette without breaking a few eggs', is a famous and rather repugnant revolutionary slogan justifying the spilling of blood which tends to follow 'revolutions' everywhere. But the blood spilled in this case was not

The freedom of the pre-revolution farmyard.

human but natural: our ancient natural habitats of wetlands and woodlands heath, downland, hedgerows and the edges of our uplands. These all started to disappear under the plough and the bulldozer. There was other long-term ecological damage including marked changes in soil structure in some very fertile counties. In parts of East Anglia the soil even started to dry out and blow away in the wind. The soil was no longer kept in good heart by good husbandry. It was only kept 'alive' by an intensive care system consisting of deep-plough surgery, drip-feed fertilizers, applications and implants of chemicals, and a transfusion of energy supplied by a constant inflow of fossil fuel.

The natural organic activity of the soil became reduced through excessive reliance on artificial additives. It became more acidic. In clay soil regions around Warwick and Northampton, after fifteen years of intensive, mechanical, one-crop agriculture, the soil deteriorated to the point where two wet seasons made efficient arable farming an uphill, water-logged struggle. Nitrogen fertilizers and heavy metal compounds became as much a part of the soil as worms once were, and they even seeped into the water table and water courses. The ploughing up and drainage of marginal areas traditionally unsuitable for crop production, led to rapid run-off and subsequent lowland flooding like that which afflicted the

Opposite
Mono-crop madness – It may look pretty efficient, but it's the ecology of the dust bowl.

The conveyor-belt of factory-farming.

Vale of York in 1983. England's great heritage landscapes, the countryside of Constable, Hardy, Brontë and Shakespeare, with their appeal to the tourist millions, were transformed overnight by the new agriculture. Ghosts of culture past were ploughed under for the ghosts of agriculture future: short-stemmed grain and short-term gain.

Just as Farmer Giles, or rather the government, the advisory bodies, bank and agro-chemical investors who were pushing him, presided over the deflowering of large parts of the countryside, replacing diversity with uniformity, multiculture with monoculture, so also they banished much of the animal life that went with it. Large numbers of our traditional birds took flight altogether or sought refuge in nature reserves. Some nineteen species of wild flowers disappeared from our shores and another fifty became threatened with extinction. These were the silent victims of the Revolution – the broken eggs.

As Farmer Giles replaced fallow, crop rotation and leguminous nitrogen-fixing with accumulative annual doses of nitrogen fertilizer and phosphates, so also he industrialized his animal production, putting his animals on to fast-feed conveyor belts to satisfy the increasingly affluent consumer's demand for cheap meat. Large numbers of pigs, hens and cattle were banished from farmyard and green fields to life inside an artificially-lit prison. Newly-developed, intensive rearing techniques led to Farmer Giles shutting out the sunlight, confining his animals to cages and stalls, time-tabled feeding with foodstuffs doctored by additives, implants of artificial growth hormones, preventative dosing with antibiotics, 'rape-racks' for mass-insemination, and to drug-induced sedation and piped music to counter the stress of life on a conveyor belt. Farmer Giles' animals had little choice but to become factory fodder, cogs in a machine-driven wheel of deprivation from their natural environments. Although a far cry from the animal welfare-ism of 'all things bright and beautiful', Farmer Giles thought he was doing his creatures great and small a big favour – laying well or putting on so much weight with the help of the new systems, they couldn't be anything else but happy.

Couldn't they? No-one knows whether animals have feelings, but they certainly have consciousness and can experience pleasure in being alive and free – as anyone who has ever let cows out to pasture after a winter in the byre will tell you. The new systems were not 'British' but brutish: offensive regimes of privation and chemical squalor. These were aimed to meet a public demand for meat which required by the 1980s the sacrificial slaughter of some 3000 beasts every minute of every working day of every year. At the heart of burgeoning public life was a conveyor belt of heartless animal privation and death.

Nature, however, has a habit of hitting back when her laws are flouted in too gross a way. Farmer Giles' prairie-grown cereals became susceptible to widespread and insistent fungal infections, the likes of which had never been seen before, and his farm animals became prey to a number of rapidly-spreading bacterial and viral infections and diseases, particularly pneumonia and hepatitis. Not only were there now more virulent strains of bacterial, fungal and viral diseases, but the natural resistance of the animals, based on genetic diversity, and built up by exercise, pure air, sunshine and the freedom of the fields had broken down altogether. To counteract these Farmer Giles was forced to invest in harder chemicals, more sprays and drenches – which have become as big a problem as the diseases they are meant to treat.

Some factory-farm induced infections, like Salmonella, were passed on to the public, and outbreaks became commonplace. And if that didn't get us, then there were the accumulative effects of the preventative anti-biotics, synthetic hormones and metallic trace elements left in the meat after slaughter to worry about. Rules, regulations, voluntary guide-lines and controls were developed for all these things. But as observation and enforcement in such a huge industry was difficult the problems did not go away and the blame always fell on the poor old farmer. Yet Farmer Giles was simply meeting demand and the interest payments on his bank loan, by the best means that modern technology and scientific advice had put at his disposal.

Not only blood was spilt on the new floor of the factory farm, but also an awful lot of energy. Animal feed is energy-expensive. It must be grown, transported and finally stored before its transformation through animal stomachs into egg-energy and quick-brew protein. No longer was the animal taken to its food, losing precious pounds in the process, the food was taken to the animal. Once there it was plastered with steroids and chemically engineered through the five-star royal showground hoops of the modern factory farm. However, any athletic energy-consuming ambitions that the food processors – the animals themselves – may have entertained, were put paid to by the runs and cages built around them.

Critics of Farmer Giles' activities point out that feeding grain to animals to convert it into fat is, in fact, an extremely inefficient means of producing people-protein. If each of Farmer Giles' customers had gone the vegan way they would have required only six sacks of pulses, beans and grains to feed them for a whole year. To obtain the same amount of food via the pig, however chemically pampered, the contents of three times that number of sacks would be required – and that's apart from all the other extra costs, like packaging, transport, veterinary fees, the butcher's cut and so on. Even worse, much of the content of these sacks comes from deplorably poor Third World countries. Put your head in any one of those sacks and it takes you right back to the wholefood shop: soya from Brazil, groundnuts from Africa, manioc from Thailand and fishmeal from Peru. It's all good, clean exotic stuff, an inter-continental breakfast culled from the cheapest sources. It doesn't matter if the people in those countries are starving. The food goes to the animal with the greatest buying power, whether it's a wholefood freak, a factory pig or a battery hen.

Farmer Giles' new system also had other environmental consequences. The factory farm began to produce intensive effluent, pure, untreated pollution in the form of 60 million tonnes of slurry, too poisonous to put back on the land and for which there existed no recognized mode or code of disposal. The factory farm began to get away with things for which an industrial polluter would have been prosecuted. But Farmer Giles' field day was not yet complete. That came with the

impact of the pesticides, herbicides and insecticides he felt forced to apply yearly to his golden grainbelts just to sustain his now accustomed high output and high bank charges. These compensated for the weakness to which the crops had become prone as a result of mono-cropping and the loss of the field-edge habitats where the natural enemies of insects and pests used to base themselves.

'Total herbicide application to pasture land.'

By the 1970s more than 240,000 hectares of British countryside were being sprayed with over 10 million gallons of toxic chemicals every year. Some crops were sprayed as many as ten times over. Pest overkill you might say, and dangerous enough to kill more than pests. 'Enough pesticides were sprayed onto vegetables to turn you into one' was not just an environmental slogan. Of the 800 chemical compounds that had been approved for aerial spraying by the Ministry, some were lethal to humankind and the warnings on the cans even said so! Particularly dangerous ones, as well as DDT which ceased to be approved but was still available, included other chlorinated hydrocarbons like Aldrin, and 24-D and 245-T which together made up the chemical defoliant, Agent Orange, used by the US against their enemy during the Vietnam War. This deadly list of poisons also included Paraquat, a chemical which attacks the skin and the lungs, and organophosphorous compounds which attack the nervous system much as their forbear, the Second World War nerve gas was intended to do. The excessive use of these chemicals had turned our countryside into a battlefield, a veritable testing ground for chemical warfare!

The chemical war against nature's pests had its well publicized human victims;

farmworkers, villagers, firemen and even little country children on the way to school. Despite guidance codes the dive bombers – helicopters, small planes and tractor sprays – could not stop their weaponry from deviating away from their strategic targets on account of wind, spray-drift and normal atmospheric conditions even on calm days. All this went not only onto and into our food, but it also went into the soil, building up residues, altering the organic make-up of the soil and killing the pest predators which nature herself had provided.

And as the pests and humans scurried for cover, so did the wildlife if it could find it. Often it didn't. As insects, earthworms and other key animals in the food chain, voles, mice, moles and rabbits were poisoned they passed the poisons onto the great birds of prey, the sparrowhawks, merlins, owls and falcons. It was feared that if the aerial bombers kept it up, one of our greatest traditional winged warriors, the barn owl, could become extinct. And by the late seventies, chemical poisoning had made a major contribution to the decline of more than 220 species of birds in Western Europe, with more than fifty threatened with extinction.

By the 1980s the manufacture of pesticides, insecticides and herbicides had become a multi-million para-national business worth an estimated 8 billion dollars, with between 8–12 million dollars spent annually on developing each new pesticide. That was a lot of jobs, a lot of investment and a lot of vested interests: it also amounted to over 30% of the variable costs of arable farming to Farmer Giles. Farmer Giles himself was reported as being not too happy with the treadmill of chemical usage upon which he now found himself trampling. The true countryman in him intuitively found it disturbing.

Some farmers even started fighting back against the pressure from the chemical giants, the agricultural advisers and the scientists, by using less and less chemicals. Friends of the Earth, some politicians and Royal Commissioners, and in 1985, some legislative amendments and controls had joined in the fightback with some success. But the really successful about-turn was masterminded by the initial enemy: the pests themselves. Insects were not the only species apart from man which were actually increasing in numbers. Over 270 kinds of insects had developed immunity against most pesticides. There was even a strain of aphid which had developed extra genes and more enzymes to break down the insecticides. As the insects began to thrive despite and in some cases thanks to the poisons which had been developed to kill them, the farmers were advised to apply more and more in even more concentrated doses.

But despite all these negative environmental and social consequences, despite the blood spilt on the farmyard floor and occasional outbreaks of guerilla warfare from the greenies and the greenflies, it was recognized that from the point of view of food production, the Third Agricultural Revolution had been a great success. And food production was, after all, the object of the exercise. In fact Farmer Giles achieved his objective so well that by 1985, there were 150 intervention stores up and down the land providing de-luxe, air-conditioned, temperature-controlled housing for some 3 million tonnes of surplus cereal, 30,000 tonnes of beef, 60,000 tonnes of butter and 32,000 tonnes of skimmed milk powder!

But these mountains of madness were dwarfed by the surpluses stockpiled in the intervention stores elsewhere in Europe. If the high production rates are sustained, it is estimated that by 1990, there will be some 80 million tonnes of surplus animal fodder lying waste, while the world's poor, and their animals, go without. Sometimes this surplus food is destroyed – an act of outrageous moral vandalism – or it is dumped on the local world market at give-away prices, having the effect of destroying local Third World markets and putting productive land out of cultivation. Why buy local produce if you could buy imported produce cheaper?

Farmer Giles had been featherbedded right the way through; he had been exempt from rates on his land and he had received tax relief on his assets and equipment. In addition, according to some sources, the total cost to the consumer and the taxpayer in supporting his activities was running at over £3$\frac{1}{2}$ billion a year by 1980.

The irony was that often he himself hadn't done that well. Not if he was a farmworker, a tenant or a small farmer, an upland, marginal or part-time farmer. Many went out of business. The bigger Farmer Giles had undoubtedly done well, but the chemical companies and the banks had done even better. By the mid 1980s the revolutionary wheel had come full circle and Farmer Giles was in danger of being knocked *off* his perch. The success of agriculture had for so long depended on excess of inputs, machinery, investment and finally, in uneconomic excess of output. Quotas and price controls were slipping in, produce by produce, and it looked like the high-input cow, the conveyor-belt pig and the hi-tech cereal could even be heading for the refuge of the *Red Data Book*. All it would take to tipple the balance would be another oil crisis like that of the late seventies. For oil, the raw material of all farm additives, had been the fuel of the farm revolution.

The story of Farmer Giles, though not finished yet, is clearly heading for a bad ending. So we leave it there, and staying within the same time span we'll go on safari and take a look at how some of his counterparts in the Third World have got on.

The British and European Agricultural Revolution and the fortunes of Farmer Giles were greatly aided by the Third World's raw materials, fodder, fuel and access to markets. The Third World did get something back — we exported factory and state farming, manufactured goods and chemicals, high technology, scientific knowledge, advice ... and when things got really uncomfortable, sticking plaster such as 'Band Aid'. After all, food for Britain should also be food for the world. But has it really happened? The true story is far more tragic than the fate of Farmer Giles.

Our visit takes us to the Sahelian Farmer Giles. He lives in either Niger, Chad, Mali or Mauritania, in an area of mixed semi-desert, temperate or tropical savannah and grassland, where the soils are shallow in depth and the land is subject to cycles of drought. But there has always been sufficient rainfall and pasture to support a substantial tribal population and abundant wildlife.

In the Sahel, as in much of the Third World, traditional forms of agriculture have been subject to 'modernization' since early colonial times. But this process took a gigantic leap forward in the late fifties and sixties. This took the form of an agricultural revolution in the developing world, led by the planting of high-yielding, quick-maturing crop varieties, backed up by an army of fertilizers, pesticides, irrigation systems and machinery. But whereas Farmer Giles seemed to benefit from the new agricultural systems, in the Sahel the changes proved disastrous. Famine struck, and in the late sixties and early seventies, many thousands of people died and millions of cattle perished. In the eighties, famine continues unabated, affecting parts of the Sahel, Ethiopia and the Sudan, and many other African states.

Prior to their 'revolution' the farmers of the Sahel were either pastoralists or cultivators, whose lifestyles had been adapted to suit their variable environment and unpredictable weather conditions. The pastoralists roamed the land with their meagre herds because it was the only way of making effective use of the scarcest and most inconsistent of their resources: rain. In the desert, it rarely rains regularly in the same place, so in order to survive, all desert-dwellers have to be sensitive to its irregularity.

Equally they have to know when to stop their animals grazing to allow re-growth in the fragile environment, and to preserve the pasture for subsequent return visits. The cattle-herders used to trade with the more settled cultivators, exchanging milk and meat products for millet or sorghum, both highly drought-resistant cereals, ecologically appropriate to local desert conditions. The diet of both groups was thus enriched and the land was fertilized by the manure of the animals grazing on the harvested millet stalks. Economy balanced ecology, and the people thrived: explorers and visitors to West and East Africa in the 19th century found a healthy local population well-adapted to living with the fragile ecology of their desert environment. The early colonials quickly changed this. They enacted quarantine laws to stop the herders from moving their animals across European-'owned' land; they induced them to auction their animals at low prices; and they forcibly grabbed the land of the cultivators, replacing the traditional desert crops with alien cash crops like cotton, tea, rubber and peanuts for export to profitable western markets.

This had two direct effects: it undermined the relationship between the herders and the cultivators, upon which the production of food for all in the Sahel was precariously balanced; it interfered with traditional trek routes, including those of migrating wildlife like the wildebeest, narrowing their range and concentrating them into insufficient land, leading to overgrazing, soil erosion and loss of animals. Some Sahelians adapted to their new circumstances by working on the huge colonial cash-crop estates and by using their earnings to supplement their much more meagre traditional livelihoods. There were many social, economic and ecological problems. But at least the colonial estates observed the principles of fallow and crop rotation, mixing cash crops with local crops like millet, and thus allowed the soil to regenerate.

This changed with the coming of agri-business just after the Second World

A cattle camp in the Sudan ... but the pastures are fast disappearing.

War and the early years of independence. Increased demand for peanuts and cotton brought with it improved seed varieties, artificial fertilizers, expatriate technical assistance, farm machinery and the laying out of vast agricultural estates. The desert was mono-cropped for money, most of it to pay taxes and to cover the cost of loans and the investment necessary to increase animal production. More and more land was put under cash-crop production, and the governments increased prices to encourage more exports rather than food for their people. Fallow went out of the window – replaced by artificial fertilizers. In 1964, a law was even passed in Senegal which discouraged fallow by taking away the ownership of any land that was not cultivated within a three-year period. All this time, the new peanut crops were quickening the loss of the soil's natural supplies of nitrogen, phosphates, potash, magnesium and lime. The land grew restless – and overhead the sun burned just as it always had, drying out the over-cropped, exhausted soils of the vast agro-estates.

As mono-cropping took over, the smaller farmers supplying the local food markets were forced to move north on to more marginal land. They were reduced, like the herders, to subsistence living, to scratching the dry soil for ever-reducing yields. Trading their produce became an impossibility: there was nothing left to trade with the pastoralists. They could not even afford the chemical inputs, the credit and even the cattle necessary to grow their own cash crops. If they did manage to take anything out of the soil they certainly weren't able to put anything back in: the soil, depleted of nutrients and protective cover, had started to erode. So also the pastoralists, confined to smaller, over-grazed grassland ranges, and denied their traditional cropland grazing on millet and sorghum stubble became increasingly unable to cope with the droughts. Previously, these cyclical patterns of good and bad years had been the environmental norm that the Sahel pastoralists faced. Now they lacked the resources to manage, and they watched helplessly as their grassland dried out, the soil loosened, and clouds of precious earth swirled away with the dry season winds. Then, between 1967 and 1972 all over the marginal lands of the Sahel, the new homelands of the

A race against time for African wildebeest as their migration routes to water are fenced off to contain cattle for distant First World markets.

pastoralists and the food crop cultivators, disaster struck: the desert rebelled and the droughts claimed human and animal lives — over 100,000 people and 3 million cattle. Thousands of children died after succumbing to measles and other diseases as a result of being weakened by malnutrition. Over many areas harvest dropped by half, and 25–40% of the animal herds were wiped out. But ironically, while the people starved, the export crops flourished. In Mali there was a 70% increase in peanut production between 1967 and 1972, and cotton production increased by an astonishing 400%.

The worldwide publicity which followed the famine led to a massive relief operation from overseas — aid. The West exported some 5 billion pounds worth of food, equipment, expertise and technology to the stricken countries in an attempt to save lives and restore the local ecological balance. And with aid came other problems. In order to meet the shortages which at that time looked like becoming annual events, the aid agencies encouraged the local farmers to grow high-yielding varieties of food crops like rice, and instituted irrigation schemes to stimulate the growth of these crops. But then, it was quickly found that irrigation schemes deprived the herders of dry-season pasture, forcing them to concentrate their grazing into even smaller areas. This simply intensified the process of ecological destruction which had been responsible for the Sahelian problem in the first place. Fragile grasslands became overgrazed, the precious relationship between herders and pastoralists became further undermined, the crop fields went without dung and the local farmers, unable to afford fertilizers became more susceptible to the predations of the large landowners, merchants and government officials. These were the very same middle-men who had initiated production for export-only in the 1950s and 1960s. Yet again, despite all the aid and the overseas goodwill, the local Sahelians stood to starve while others profited.

The supreme irony of the entire Sahelian aid episode was the fact that rice, a plant which depends on a lot of water, was proffered as a replacement for the relatively drought-resistant sorghum and millet, to a people living in one of the most drought-prone regions in the world! Needless to say, many people of the Sahel, along with other Africans are now dependent upon imported rice supplies, which increase overseas debt, rather than on local supplies.

Such problems are echoed across the countries of the Third World, even in lush, tropical climates of countries like Brazil. Here, in order to produce sugar cane for export, the land was stripped of trees, the soil was deprived of its nutrients and the local farmers were not allowed to spare any land for the cultivation of food crops or even for the growing of fruit trees. The result was again malnutrition and famine. While sugar production peaked at 96 million tonnes a year by the mid 1970s, malnutrition gathered apace, affecting 75% of the population. The so-called 'Green Revolution' of Brazil and the Sahel was not green, but grey and dry, a hollow, crumbling irony. It has had a disastrous effect on not just these countries but global ecology as a whole. Currently more than 30 million square kilometres, approximately 20% of the earth's surface, is under direct threat of desertification. Over 80 million people live on this threatened land. And the problem threatens to worsen: world-wide, nearly 21 million hectares of land have been reduced to a state of agricultural uselessness.

In the dry states of Africa, once the protective soil cover was broken, it was simply whipped away by the wind and washed by torrential rain into gulleys and rivers and eventually into the sea. The Sahel had the worst area of wind erosion on earth. Asia as a whole is now thought to be losing 25 billion tonnes of topsoil a year. It takes 100–2500 years for 2.5 centimetres of topsoil to form, but the same amount can be lost within a few years. If current trends of soil-loss continue the world stands to lose over 275 million by the year 2000 – 18% of its arable lands. By the year 2025, only twenty-five years later, we could stand to lose the same amount again. And this is apart from natural processes of desertification. At this rate, 'Dune', the dry planet, would cease to be science fiction and become scientific fact, not a story of outer space, but the true story of *Spaceship Earth*.

The wildlife of the Third World has suffered too. Desertification has destroyed habitats. Soil erosion has blown apart the natural food chain of prey and predator; deforestation for food, intensive monocropping and pesticide poisoning have eliminated breeding grounds; natural cycles of eco-compensation have been undermined, creating new, less-manageable pests – there are no longer enough birds to eat the locusts. The overall stock of species is being reduced at a rate of over one a day, with some 1 million species threatened with extinction. Traditional breeds of domestic animals have disappeared in favour of high-yielding, high-energy dependent hybrids. As the wilderness areas of the Third World have retreated under this advancing tide of uniform agricultural development, so its animals have been forced to seek refuge in game parks and animal sanctuaries: artificially controlled and shrinking environments which are subject to other pressures like tourism and poaching.

The fate of the Kalahari wildebeest exemplifies this process at its worst. For centuries, herds of this magnificent wild buffalo migrated annually across the plains of the Kalahari following the seasonal rains which fill shallow pans and waterholes, and replenish the grass. They moved north in the dry season, and south when the rains came; the fragile desert ecology remained intact and the herds thrived. They provided game for carnivorous animals and man alike, part of the make-up of the dry wilderness. But in the 1960s, cattle-breeding in Botswana suddenly boomed, providing beef for the export market and the food mountains of Europe and the USA. It had become a vital part of the economy of this poor country, though ironically, more than half the people are dependent on food aid from overseas. By the 1980s, the number of cattle in Botswana had exceeded 3 million head, outnumbering the wildebeest, trampling down and grazing off the precious sandveld, but not moving on and allowing it to replenish. The cattlemen, in order to minimize the spread of foot-and-mouth disease, put up fences in the desert: permanent barriers to the free movement of the wildebeest along their traditional dry-season routes. Trapped behind fences, cut off from water and pasture, the wildebeest roamed aimlessly in the desert searching for an increasingly rare combination of water, shade and food. In 1980 and again in 1983 thousands upon thousands perished in the desert. At one point the stench was so bad that the cattlemen collected their bodies and cremated them in a huge pyramid, a funeral pyre for a vanishing animal.

In 1984 not a single wildebeest was seen travelling north. Extinction for the straggling herds which remain is almost a matter of time. The wildebeest will be Africa's bison, the great Plains Buffalo of the North American West, cornered and hunted into the history books and collections of zoo oddities. The African wildebeest, whose plight is shared by many other species of Third World wildlife, had fallen victim to agricultural 'progress', the shifting sands of agri-business.

By the 1980s agri-business had become survival for many in the Third World, and it had fostered the growth of the independent nation state, free from the chains of colonialism. But taken to excess, as in the desert states, it had undermined sensitive ecosystems, making them vulnerable to minor climatic variations and threatening the survival of all, animals and people. And it had

An awe-inspiring landscape … but deforestation and over-intensive land-use in Nepal are eating away at a fragile ecology and threatening future food production.

fomented discontent, warfare and revolution. Agri-business had become agro-business, a pest.

'Agro-business' brought with it another ecological pest: pesticides. In a desperate attempt to control disease and maintain high crop yields for export, the Third World became addicted to the use of ever more and more imported fertilizers. Governments, farmers and their national advisers became under constant pressure from the huge international chemical giants to purchase an ever-burgeoning variety of poisons including many that were banned or considered unsafe for use in the west, like DDT and Galecron.

Safety standards in the Third World have always been low. Crops were sprayed indiscriminately, over wildlife, fields, houses and people. The warnings on the canisters were usually in a foreign language or were meaningless to illiterate land workers. In 1981, Oxfam reported that over 950,000 cases of accidental pesticide poisoning were occurring every year. Blood samples from Latin-American land workers showed them to have eleven times as much DDT in their bodies as the average North American. Protective clothing was rarely supplied, and was usually unsuitable for tropical climates. One Mexican field worker claimed that he received several pesticide showers every day, but said he had to get used to it because if he became ill there would be no money. If he got weaker he would lose his job. Ironically, most of the produce subjected to this rain of chemicals is sold to and consumed by those countries where those self-same chemicals were banned. In time, the chemicals wiped out the natural predators of the plant pests while the pests themselves, the malaria-resistant mosquito, the encephalitis mosquito, spruce budworm, spider mites, brown plant-hopper, and cotton whitefly built up resistance.

It became veritable bug-bomb: the number of species resistant to chemical insecticides rose from an estimated 7 in 1938 to 432 in 1980, directly proportionate to the more intensive development and application of more and more chemicals every year. In this ever-widening circle of poison and pest, which has become the greater pest? Our African Safari, far from giving us vistas of luxurious game reserves and a food production paradise, leaves us with a bad taste in our own well-fed mouths and a hollow feeling in the pits of our otherwise well-fed stomachs.

There is no doubt, that on the whole, large-scale agricultural development has increased the food stock of the global garden and improved on Mother Nature's potential to provide for human sustenance. But look at some of the side effects: mass starvation in the Sahel and Ethiopia, mass malnutrition in South America; the destruction of the world's last wilderness areas: gross social and economic inequalities; luxury foods being exported from starving nations; widespread pollution from pesticide production and application, desertification and global ecological disruption.

Our quick passage through the post-war world of food production gives us an impression of a world still at war, at war with its children and with its environment. It is a slow, cruel and relentless war, fought without much resistance and with many casualties, many of them still to be counted. The

casualties in the war include our children's natural heritage, the diverse countryside of earlier pre-war childhoods in the First and Third Worlds, and the
ecological balance on which their future health and all future food production
depends. But the casualties also include the hundreds of thousands of innocents
who die every year from the effects of famine and malnutrition. Post-war
agricultural progress, fuelled by cheap energy and the entrepreneurial trading
power of the industrial nations, has failed the children of the world and laid waste
to large parts of their environmental heritage.

Africa has been worst hit. It is fast losing the ability to feed itself. In 1984, 140
million out of 531 million people were dependent on grain imported from
abroad, and this figure is likely to double as the deserts spread and the aid
programmes proliferate. Some 10 million people left their traditional villages by
1986 for the sanctuary of temporary camps. Relief aid is 'free' but a lot of food is
imported for sale, and the bill for this has risen ninefold from 600 million dollars
in 1972. Servicing these debts decimates earnings from exports and increases
dependency on the First World. Even the World Bank, a major donor and lender,
and a major contributor to the spread of large-scale growth and the ideologies of
agricultural 'progress', now admits that in Africa, its policies have failed. It has
been a very unwise lender, encouraging the bankruptcy of a continent, the
de-stocking of its traditional food supplies.

*All these revolutions have clearly stunted the long-term growth of the global garden. We
must go elsewhere in search of an antidote, of agricultural systems which offer ecological stability.*

PLANTING A FUTURE

While the post-war upheavals were taking place in European and Third-World
agriculture, a different kind of green revolution was starting in a few hidden
corners of our own backyards. It is now beginning to break the bonds of obscurity
and become a force to reckon with. It's called organic agriculture, a holistic
system of agricultural theory and practice, which in the 1980s has at last found its
time. There is great public interest in its practices and an increasing public
demand for its products, but as yet, both its profile and levels of investment and
development are low. So to find out how it works we have to go back to the hills
where it is mainly practised.

*Come with us on two short trips to two of the finest examples of British agricultural
landscapes: the rolling hills and smooth valleys of West Wales; and the glorious
uplands of North Yorkshire, where heather moor meets grassy dale.*

We've arrived at the farm of Patrick Holden, the chairman of a national organic
farmers' association, who maintains a modest 130 dairy holding which allows
living room for not just cows but hordes of bumble-bees and meadow flowers,
sky-larks and meadow pipits. The air of Patrick's estate is alive with birds and

insects: and the earth itself is alive too: the fields and hedges are teeming with
green clover sward and activity – both animal and human. It's like childhood
re-visited: the fresh smell and sounds of the countryside all around you. And it's
not just a pretty picture, it's a rigorously efficient, working landscape which
makes money and grows good, green, wholesome food. Patrick is standing by the
gate and telling us that he's been on this farm for eleven years without using a
single bag of nitrogen or a single pesticide spray:

> 'We rely on clover for nitrogen fixation and this will give us at least 250 units
> of nitrogen to the acre. We do bring in natural supports to growth, like rock
> phosphates and rock potash, but only to feed the soil, not the plants. We
> develop the potential of the soil itself to release its own nutrients and re-cycle
> and develop those nutrients. That's the key principle of organic farming.'

Feeding the soil? That's rich. But it works. Patrick's soil supports almost two
cattle units for every hectare of grass which is very high in such a marginal area.
That's plenty of milk for you and me, as good as most chemical farms at their
best, and no silly surpluses for the EEC. And it all comes down to good
husbandry, the marriage of man the farmer, with all his wits and elbow grease, to
the most beautiful bride of all – Mother Earth. It's not all cosmic spirals, there's
carrots too. You can't beat carrots for good old down-to-earth vegetableism, and
Patrick grows lots of them. The carrot he holds out to the chemical farmer is dark
orange and juicy, with all the taste and smell of the earth, and he gets 12 tonnes to
the acre. What about the weeding, you will say, and the carrot fly?

> 'No problem', says Patrick – 'We weed the carrots early on, once by hand and
> once by flame thrower, before the seedlings emerge; and the good healthy soil
> we cultivate, and rotations we follow, keep out the carrot fly.'

With his cows and his carrots, Patrick Holden makes a good living, debts to
the bank are lowering whereas the debts of many of his chemical-farmer counterparts are getting worse. There are no chemical residues or preservatives on his
food. People can't get enough of it; his market is a growing one. There's no
question of robbing the resources of other sectors either, as there is no reliance on
high, energy-expensive inputs from oil or the Third World – except for the diesel
he needs to keep his small tractor chugging along.

*We leave Patrick to go and see his close friend and colleague, Peter Segger, chairman
of a sister organic group, an organic growers' association.*

Peter lives nearer to the coast, and he, too, farms organically, producing a wide
range of vegetables without doing anything to bolster the profits of the agro-
chemical firms or to poison the earth. Down on Peter's farm the birds sing too.
Peter knows his organic onions well; all his vegetables – onions, carrots, potatoes
and greens – are all gently raised from well-tidied, carefully-laid, raised beds.
These are separated by paths so there's no tractor wheels or heavy feet to trample
down the plant root growth. Peter's organic system is however no 'back to nature'

wizardry, more a combination of old organic axioms, – a well-fed soil, with lots of rich compost earthworms, a bit of lime – and sound scientific experiment. A good example of this is in his hot-houses, a concession to intensive production you might say, but one where nature and culture are brought together to full effect.

'Conventionally, growers have to water their lettuces a lot to keep 'em cool and wet. But you tend to get fungal diseases in damp hot conditions, and the chemical man has to bring in the fire engines – fungicides – to control the outbreak. We don't do that, we make the plant grow deeply, water it when it goes in, and lay down lots of organic matter to keep the surface dry, the moisture in and the roots deep down.'

And there you have it, magic strong green lettuces, and if the roots are like tree trunks it doesn't matter, because you don't eat those anyway. Peter and Patrick do have some problems, but no more than their chemical competitors, and because of the total lack of long-term research into organic methods they farm and grow by trial and error: a constant learning and growing curve. But the problems are outweighed by the benefits. Energy and input costs are low; the yields are sometimes low too, but the returns are higher because their market is firm, their products high quality, and their prices compete well with their competitors. They employ more people too, twice as many as the conventional farmer. The public can't get enough of their produce, so together they had to devise their own national distribution and registration system, to make sure that as many people as possible can eat organically and naturally British.

A sense of community and successful and productive organic farming methods come together at Botton village in the north of England.

Right The Botton cows are unpolled, and yield chemical-free dairy produce.

Theirs is an ecological approach to food production, the answer to many of the ills which currently beset modern European agriculture. They are unaffected by pesticide and chemical controls or by quotas. They don't destroy wildlife habitats; they don't pollute the streams and rivers; they don't produce unwanted foods – there could never be an organic food mountain; they don't depopulate the countryside and don't exhaust the earth's available energy resources. And *they* make the profits rather than the chemical companies. Today West Wales, tomorrow the world: Peter Segger says –

'The implications are enormous, but we start off by working on our own farms. From our own farms we develop systems we feel confident about. From that it develops up into a national policy. The implications then become international.

'We are trying to find the parameters for a new approach to agricultural policy which takes into account all the problems that agriculture has run into. If we can get our parameters right – get rid of pollution, rely less on production subsidies, look after wildlife, make maximum use of resources on the farm, minimize external inputs, look after food quality, rural employment and the social and cultural life of the countryside – then we can start to look at an agricultural policy which would be right for the EEC, this country and elsewhere. If you have a right idea, do it locally and having shown it can be done, do it nationally and internationally.'

From small healthy acorns, tall strong powerful oaks grow. So maybe there is a chance that the global garden can become green. And there's that message again,

'think globally, act locally'. Organic farming has never received the proper support it deserves from governments, university research departments and the official advisory agencies themselves. In this case, it's the officials that are the stick-in-the-muds: so far they are not taking enough notice of the organic systems that are flourishing before their eyes. But with the wind changing, maybe some of the cobwebs which the vested chemical interests help weave over their eyes will begin to be blown away.

After that heady bout of idealism and hope, it's time to go up to Danby in the misty Yorkshire Moors, and see how an entire organic community is making out on a diet of fresh air and organic eating.

At the top of the dale lies Botton Village, a straggling collection of houses and farmsteads which centres on a community chapel and meeting place. It's the home of 300 people, a thriving community where some 150 voluntary co-workers and their children (receiving no salary or national insurance stamps) look after one another and a resident population of 150 villagers – handicapped adults from the outside world who have been found a permanent home, and a place to belong. It's an 'organic' working and living system. The community's food is provided by an organic agricultural method which thrives on the poor peaty soils of a very marginal area, yet produces enough vegetables to fill their tables and their tummies throughout the year. All their vegetable wastes go back into the soil, there's room for wildlife and work for the people. Its idyllic, a beautiful place, a paradise of flower-filled field and hedgerows, woody nooks and watery crannies for the children who grow up there.

The agricultural system of Botton village is in fact a variation on the organic theme, called 'bio-dynamic' farming and gardening. This works on the understanding that the earth and soil are living, breathing entities, a mass of organisms, each of which is related to the other and also to everything else within the immediate environment of the farm or garden. According to Botton farmer Paul Martin –

> 'A bio-dynamic farmer is more concerned with creating a balance for the plant, a balance between all the forces of nature and the environment which play on it. The farm itself is a self-contained organism. We try to farm properly without taking excess from what the land can provide. We provide a place for everybody, where they can work and live, and a place for nature too. The social aspect of the farm is just as important as the cows, the hay and the silage. We do use machines and hand tools, but no more than we need, and sufficient to keep people in work with dignity.'

Bio-dynamic growers have discovered that if you grow plants alongside other plants, and in specific relation to certain natural features like tree-lines, hillsides, and water courses, you can obtain a good healthy growth and minimize on disease and infection. They optimize not just the soil condition and the protection of the plants, but the overall nature and shape of the environment in which they are grown. They do this for animals too; and farms and gardens are placed alongside one another, so that the wastes from each can be used to fertilize or provide food for the other. It's an environmentally-integrated, holistic system of growth.

There's more to it than meets the eye. There's a holistic philosophy behind the growth at Botton. According to Paul Martin –

'A farm has so much more to offer humanity as a whole than just an area of scenic beauty where food is produced. It has so many healing and calming properties. These have to be brought to the fore, and it's the farmer's task to realize the full potential of the farm beyond simply food production.'

The produce – the vegetables, milk, cheeses, eggs and meat – taste good and do you good. And the environment looks healthy too – a patchwork of fields and meadows, gardens, woodland and natural features. Whether you're there at midsummer or midwinter, when they light garden bonfires that fill the sky with sparks and laughter, or in the middle of a rainy week, it's magic, sound environmental magic. There's not much muck in sight and there's no mystery – it works.

It's all right for them up there in the wilds, cut off from the troubles of the real world, what about us down here in the cities? What good are that lot doing for us? The fact is, the people of Botton and the other one hundred odd communities like them across the globe, do a lot of good. Not only are they looking after people whom modern society has rejected and would rather shut away and ignore, but they produce good healthy food, preserve a rural environment which would otherwise be threatened by intensive agriculture, and contribute to the depleting stock of human and environmental well-being and happiness. Two weeks spent digging vegetables in a place like that would make you and us into changed people. Botton, founded in 1955 as the very first community of its kind in the world, has been spawning mini-Bottons all over the world, from Yorkshire to Switzerland and Minnesota, USA. A recent project is the foundation of a new community in nearby Cleveland on the outskirts of urban Middlesbrough, an area of great urban depression and unemployment. The new community is to be based at Larchfield Farm, on land given by an enlightened borough council and with the full blessing of all sections of the community.

Ironically, Larchfield Farm has a panoramic view of the ICI chemical works at Tees-side, one of the largest agro-industrial conurbations in the UK. Every day the vast cooling towers, steel chimneys and aluminium flues of the ICI chemical plants pour out clouds and clouds of smoke, heat and vapour, destined for who knows where. But in that heart of industrial darkness and in urban Tees-side's dying day – as plant gets moved abroad and jobs are lost – there is hope: the new organic spirit of Larchfield Farm. Even the soil is beginning to look more cheerful. After decades of nitrogen and fungicides, it is being weaned back into a living condition by the fallow method and lots of living compost. According to the new farmers, the land suffered symptoms of withdrawal when it was first deprived of its routine chemical 'fix'. But the organisms and worms are again beginning to turn, and prospects for an early harvest look good. Larchfield is no rural retreat though. It's an urban farm, intended to provide produce for the community, for urban youngsters, a home for the handicapped, and a chance for those who have been very deprived, to work and live again with nature in their hearts, and with a renewed soil, new ground, under their feet.

West Wales, North Yorkshire, Industrial Tees-side, these are all small beginnings, but they do show a positive way forward for people and the environment, and a way out of our current mess. Not much objective research has been done to verify the success of their food production systems. But we do know some things:

In 1981 the US Department of Agriculture undertook a study which compared chemical with modern organic methods. They found that organic farming was more competitive. It was two and a half times more productive per unit of energy consumed than chemical farming (energy costs of controlling soil erosion and water pollution were taken into consideration). In the mid 1970s when the corn belt was struck by drought, the organic farmers, with their deeper-rooted crops fared well: producing higher yields than their competitors. Another study, by Washington University showed that organic farmers used only 40% of the energy needed by conventional farms. Similar studies in Europe and the USA had similar findings – flouting the scepticism of agricultural research bodies and farming associations, many of which are tied to the agro-chemical companies for funds, subsidies and jobs for their graduates or members. And the documents supporting the energy efficiency of organic agriculture continue to pile up; from the Department of Applied Economics at Cambridge, from the Dutch Agriculture Ministry in 1973; the French Government in 1975, and the New York State College of Agriculture and Life Sciences, Cornell University, in 1983. Even the UK Government's own Rothamsted Experimental Station has conducted experiments which have demonstrated that natural manure is as effective as artificial fertilizer.

If the organic method is indeed more energy-efficient, it is also kinder to the resources of the earth. It re-uses its own wastes, so there are no pollution problems. It binds rather than dries out the soil, so there are no erosion problems. It encourages rather than destroys wildlife habitats, so there are no angry conservationists to worry about. And the food produced, while it may look less uniform than its chemical equivalent, has a lower water content so it stores well and tastes richer. It is clear – organically clear – that chemical agriculture couldn't beat this long list of gains. If another Agricultural Revolution is indeed at hand, it looks increasingly as if it might be organic or semi-organic. And if the overfed, over-feathered agricultural industry is to survive into the next century it is going to have to scale its operations accordingly. The adoption of organic practices now would smooth the passage, cushion the blow, benefit the environment and ensure the survival of the smaller farmer and the rural community.

What about the rest of the world, still suffering, and heavily dependent upon food aid, the grain trade and the constant expansion of high-yielding crop production to feed the export market? Would an organic revolution, or even the introduction of simply a more balanced, more ecological sustainable industrial agriculture benefit them? The irony here is that the rest of the world has in fact

Planting rice in the traditional 'organic' way – the farmers have resisted bribes from Government agencies to experiment with pesticides, chemical fertilizers and mono-crops for years.

been farming organically for centuries, and although there have been many problems of starvation and disease in history, the mass starvation on the scale we are witnessing in Ethiopia, the Sahel and other places is fairly recent. Some parts of the Third World have stayed resolutely organic. In the Kumaon Himalayas in Northern India, the local farmers get two high-yielding harvests from the same land every year, using totally organic traditional agricultural methods. The land is terraced and irrigated using ingenious, centuries-old systems of mini-dams, ducts and water channels. The soil is fed with green and cattle manure, mulches, woodfire ash and burnt stubble. It is ploughed with oxen and weeded by hand. It's labour-intensive: there's plenty to do but also times when there's nothing to do but sit and watch the crops grow. There's also time to observe a rigorous cycle of festivals, many of which have the specific objective of improving fertility and crop growth. Well, somehow it all seems to work: every year the soil yields its bounties, a double harvest of golden, glowing winter wheat in the spring and milk pearls of rice in the autumn, as it has over the centuries.

The farmers of Kumaon know the fragility of their environment intimately and have systematically rejected the bribes from outside. An Indo-European Agricultural Development Agency in the area has been trying for over fifteen years to persuade the hill farmers to experiment with nitrogen fertilizers, weedkillers and dwarf varieties of high-yielding rice in order to improve their output – and give custom to the urban manufacturers. With the exception of their own experimental farms in Kumaon, the developers have not been successful. The reaction of one farmer gives the reason why:

'Where would I get the money every year to pay for these fertilizers from? What work would we have left to do if a chemical was to kill the weeds? Where would we get straw for our cattle and manure for our fields if we grew rice that didn't have stalks? Where would be the good in all that?'

What the Kumaon hill farmer was pointing out was the effective overall harmony of his traditional, mixed-farming system: man, animals, soil, crops and even fields and trees were inseparable and harmonious components of a single system. The effectiveness of this traditional system was noticed by early visitors to India. In 1889, Dr John Voelcker of the Royal Agricultural Society of England toured the rice and wheat fields of the sub-continent and concluded that –

'The Indian raiyat or cultivator is quite as good as, and in some respects, the superior of, the average British farmer ... Nowhere would one find better instances of keeping land scrupulously clean from weeds, of ingenuity in device of water-raising appliances, of knowledge of soils and their capabilities as well as of the exact time to sow and to reap, as one would in Indian Agriculture, and this not at its best alone, but at its ordinary level. It is wonderful, too, how much is known of rotation, the system of mixed crops and

Ploughing with bullocks, Kumaon, India.

of fallowing. Certain it is that I, at least, have never seen a more perfect picture of careful cultivation, combined with hard labour, perseverance and fertility of resource, than I have seen at many of the halting places in my tour. Such are the gardens of Mahi, the fields of Nadiad and many others.'

Praise indeed for traditional ecological agriculture. But that was in the past. What about the present and the future? Fortunately much of traditional rural India sustains its very high population on a subsistence agriculture which most people would find medieval but is undeniably effective. The problems only really set in when large land-owners start to take over and amalgamate smaller holdings or when natural disaster strikes, a prolonged drought or earthquake or heavy monsoon rains causing flooding – and of course some of these are aided by man or his activities, like the deforestation of the Himalayas.

Organic farming is also making a comeback in Europe and America. In the UK alone there are now more than 600 organic or bio-dynamic farms which are registered with the Soil Association, a voluntary organic standards authority and the numbers are growing weekly. Also many of the UK's traditional hill farmers still follow the tradition of 'dog-and-stick' husbandry, eschewing the use of chemicals which upset the precarious soil balance of our heather uplands, and keeping their stock of sheep 'free range' on the hills. Where you still see hill shepherds stalking the hills with their crooks and their dogs, that is where you will find the organic methods – and a rosy glow on their cheeks.

One Third World country which is encouraging its traditional, organically-based agricultural system to be as efficient as possible, is China. As a result, the agricultural achievements of the country in the last decade have been nothing short of miraculous. In a country once plagued by famines, floods, droughts, constant food crises and a land-less peasantry, there is now full employment and food for all: no-one goes hungry. Incredible, but how was that done and so quickly?

The pace was determined by the government itself responding to needs, and by the ready availability of human energy, millions of it. From the outset, the Chinese national and local administrations were denied the opportunity and resources to adopt high-cost and capital-intensive farming methods. They worked out their own programme of growth. Land was reclaimed, rivers dammed and irrigation canals dug, all by hand.

Available resources were re-distributed and credit was made available, the land was fertilized with vegetable waste and manures. Pests and weeds were kept down with rotations and the practice of fallow. And crop wastes were fed to the animals who in turn did the necessary for the good of the soil. As a result of all this good husbandry the fertility of the soil improved a hundredfold and room was left for wildlife. To re-adapt its former leader's famous dictum, China has indeed let more than 'a hundred flowers bloom'. This part of the global garden is certainly flourishing: China produced over 305 million tonnes of cereals in 1978 and over 407 million tonnes in 1984, a 33% increase in production over six years. And where in some marginal places, there was only one harvest of wheat or rice a year, now there are two. The Chinese model – which feeds, houses and even fuels (with help from bio-gas and coppice wood) over one fifth of the world's population — is a lesson for us all.

The Chinese model is an agri-ecosystem which integrates crop-growing, stock husbandry, fish-raising and renewable energy. Each group of households and villages produces its own food, fertilizer and energy, and exports surpluses to the nearby towns. The countryside settlements even have their own light industries and the countryside looks like a well-tended garden. Even the urban factory workers are given a share in the garden, their own farm plots. It all hangs together well, bringing people and the urban and rural communities closer to one another. There is a lot of freedom for local decision-making, within an overall doctrine of collective responsibility which takes full account of local needs and local environmental conditions and contraints. The ultimate unit of production and living is the individual household — much as in the west — but it is a household where close interdependence with the wider group and the environment itself, is a condition of survival and well-being.

The rest of the world may be a long way from the once red road to China, but it is clear that we do need a revolution, a new agricultural revolution. We have to learn to feed the soil rather than the profit accounts of the chemical companies; to grow plants that are suited or adapted to their environment; to use natural and biological controls, scientifically applied, rather than chemicals, to control pests; to use nature's methods of nitrogen-fixing and energy-enhancement, fallow, crop rotation and leguminous crop-breeding; to use our genetic reservoirs of plants and systems of sympathetic plant-growing to speed growth and provide cover against soil erosion; to re-discover 'free-range' animal husbandry which benefits the soil and doesn't cause cruelty; perhaps even eat less meat like the Norwegians to cut down the energy consumption which goes into animal feedstuffs.

To mixed farming systems in the First World, a proper balance of 'horn and corn', plough and dung, could also be added increased farm diversification. Our farms have the capacity to produce a wider range of foods than have been traditionally encouraged by subsidies, including herbs, bio-gas crops, trees, shrubs and that most nutritious of all animal fodder — meadow grass. More varied farming techniques and a diverse farming landscape would attract more visitors to the countryside, increase tourist and business activity, and create work for artisans and craftworkers catering to the needs of the leisure as well as the food industries.

In the Third World there must be a move away from cash-cropping for export to local crops for local people. Small-scale farming must replace macrocropping, possibly on the Chinese model. The state and the overseas investment agencies could help by setting up regional development boards which provide credit and subsidies, advice, research, land tenure intervention, transport and local market-ing facilities for the sale and exchange of food and goods. There should also be some agricultural specialization to suit local ecological conditions. Coppice woodland cultivation in the tropics would create fuel-wood and bio-mass. Grazing should be concentrated in temperate grasslands with drier pastures being allowed to recover from over-grazing by being farmed as natural game parks and wilderness areas.

All this doesn't mean going back to nature, to back-breaking hoeing and collecting berries from the forest floor. Ecological agriculture can be scientific, using advances in plant genetics, modern machinery and scientific methods — even computers. What it does mean though, is that we have to develop a food-production system which works with, rather than against the environment, that is naturally, as well as economically sustainable. In the First World, surpluses and the chemical companies might lose out, but the farmer wouldn't: a study at Iowa University in 1974, on a more ecological approach to agriculture, predicted that it would lead to a slight drop in production and slightly higher prices but a 25% higher income for the farmers. The taxpayer would benefit too, as fewer subsidies would be paid to farmers by the government. Food would be produced to meet the needs of the people, for both the people who produce it, and the ones who consume the products.

A 'Fourth Agricultural Revolution' would open up what Professor Lawrence Roche has called a 'second front' in agricultural research and development in the countries hardest hit by the worst side effects of change in the post-war era. He believes that this would complement the positive achievements which have been made by agri-business. In Africa he sees a prominent role for a programme of re-afforestation in the deforested dry lands, and a place for familiar, more organic, traditional forms of food production. In his own words

'This second front will concentrate on small-scale farming systems and community needs; research and development programmes will include those neglected plants traditionally valued by local communities. It will ensure the conservation of the natural forest estate and the management of rangelands and give greater attention than ever before to small-scale farming systems and to providing rural people with fuel-wood, food and fodder while protecting vitally important catchment areas and arresting soil erosion. Forestry in all its ramifications must become an integral part of agricultural development in African states in the future.'[9]

A Fourth Agricultural Revolution could not be led by traditional types of revolutionary ideology, whether capitalist or socialist, whether private sector or state-led. Huge corporate bodies and businesses would simply lead us back along the dust-stained, blood-spattered road of over-intensive, over mechanized industrial agriculture, driven to feed debt repayments and export markets. Food production systems which concentrate production power in the hands of small private or national elites simply encourage selfish profit and power through the generation of scarcity and the internationalization of food control.

We do, however, need a set of international ground rules for green food growth to re-stock the global garden and puts its boundary fences and planting systems back in order. We would hesitate to recommend to anyone another CAP — a Common Agricultural Policy — which was wrongly constituted to benefit a limited First World elite. What we do need is a World Agricultural Policy — a WAP. This could be constituted differently and more openly than CAP and used to beat the elitism of the First World and the great multi-national food corporations, into ensuring a fairer distribution of food. WAP would set guidelines for sustainable production, for improving local output through enhancing traditional systems of production, for feeding the world and doing less harm to the environment. The global ground rules established by WAP would have their counterpart in local-level ground rules which put ecologically sustainable policies into practice. A first principle in this field would have to be 'Food First'. Domestic food needs would be met before anything was exported, before export-based high profits were made. There would be more local-level democratization of food production, supply and trade, which would be recognized internationally, enshrined in international law – a 'Bill of Rights to Eat'.

There is no country in the world in which the people could not feed themselves from their own resources. The structures of production, trade and supply must be changed to accommodate that fact. And keeping people free from hunger, preventing other Sahels, other Ethiopias, is wholly complementary to safeguarding the world's agricultural environment. A truly global food policy would take us someway back to the garden. That way everyone, garden, gardeners and their children would have the opportunity to really flourish, and grow.

From the global garden we can now return to the local scene where our two gardeners have been dozing in the afternoon sun after their sojourn to the pub. No prizes for guessing that it was the organic gardener, Paul, by far the fitter of the two, who was first there, the first to quaff his real ale.

GEORGE: (waking up) Maybe there's something to what you say after all; there's a bit of a funny smell from those chemicals; and I've got a plague of aphids.

PAUL: Nature's way is always better, and if we look after her properly, scientifically sustaining her, we're bound to benefit. If only the powers-that-be would take heed, we'd all benefit. Tell you what. If you give me some more of your tomatoes for my compost heap, I'll give you some ladybirds to eat your aphids!

4 THE WATER OF LIFE

BUT IS IT SAFE TO DRINK?

Water is the blood of life, yet civilization uses it in a profligate manner. The merciless pollution of our seas, lakes, rivers and even rain supply, accumulates a host of hidden dangers for the future, endangering our own health and the well-being of a whole range of water-based eco-systems.

We now take an intravenous journey through the water supply, from raindrop to seascape, charting the uses and abuses to which we subject the blood of life. We look for signs of a clean-up, at plans and paths of purification.

Clearly we cannot go on injecting poison into our common blood stream. What is the healthy solution? Do we go on leaching some of the poisons out or should we change our habits and attitudes at source and bring about a complete transfusion?

A PRECIOUS COMMODITY

The world's waterways – its springs, streams, rivers, ponds, lakes and seas – are the legacy of life itself. The water story starts as a shower of sparkling raindrops which fall and water the dry earth. The water collects in the hills and mountains of the world. Clear, fresh, oxygenated streams plunge from their upland sources to form majestic, meandering rivers, carving passages through the lands below to panoramic estuaries. There the sweet waters of the land mix with the salt of the sea, the silent process of evaporation lifts the surplus waters back into the sky. Clouds of vapour form, ready to be carried across the land and sea and fall as droplets of rain. The cycle is complete.

Water is the foundation of life on earth; without it there would be no plants, no animals, no living thing. Many of us take it for granted, because it is always there – a seemingly infinitely-renewable resource – ready and waiting at our convenience. But in many parts of the world, water is a rare commodity and precious thing, more valuable than gold; it has to be caught and conserved or even mined with drills, rigs, boreholes and windpumps. Drought leads to disease, starvation and even death.

Even in the wettest areas of the developed world, water is much more precious than most of us think. It may be the commonest substance on the face of a planet we curiously have named 'Earth', but 97.4% of it is undrinkable – tainted by too much salt. We must thank the laws of nature that evaporation leaves the salt behind and puts sweet water into cycle once more. Much of the water falls

straight back into the sea, some is locked up in polar ice. Some sinks down beneath the land lost as subterranean water. Only 8% of the water which falls from the sky is easily accessible, and that flows as quickly as it can into the sea. Life on land (and that includes over 4 billion human lives) has to catch what it can.

It's no wonder that we make intensive use of all the fresh water to which we do have access. Unfortunately use and abuse goes hand in hand. Even the resources of the sea – which covers five-sevenths of the earth, are now so abused by man that the world's fisheries are in decline and many of its creatures – whales, dolphins, seals and even some sea-birds – face the waterless grave of extinction.

Come with us downriver on a journey through our water cycle and system of supply. We're at the start of a rough and tumbling, picturesque passage, past dreaming spires, sullen docks, rolling home-counties countryside, the streets of London and the houses of Parliament to the deep salty sea – unless we get evaporated on route.

The water's cold, but not so unfamiliar – we are after all two-thirds water ourselves, and according to Darwin, water was our original home. Up in the

Water – the most precious commodity on earth bursts over an American desert at the start of the water cycle.

On the banks of the River Stour, England ... but the outfall downriver is not quite so idyllic.

headlands it's quite clean too. There's no pollution, and the duck droppings that have just landed on your head are good nutritious organic waste, containing all those things like potassium, nitrogen and phosphate which are essential to plant-growth and to making the living world go round.

To the uninitiated aquanaut the river may look a bit murky, and all this green slimy stuff, these weeds and creepy crawlies, may look nasty, but they all have their part to play in the life of the river, keeping the water pure so that we lucky humans can drink it. At this point in the water cycle nothing goes to waste. The minerals in the water feed the plants which in turn produce oxygen which in turn allows the fish to 'air' their gills and live. Any healthy river supports a chain of life, from microscopic plankton through a myriad of life forms to the fish and noble otter, all reliant on each other for their survival. It's a system in living balance: break any link in the chain and much more than the local otter population may pay the price.

It's all quite idyllic really – so far. Even in this headwater, the river ripples a primeval hymn, echoes of an ancient time before people came upon the earth. But the dream is soon shattered by the unmistakeable stench and foam of the river's first infall of pollution which we are fast approaching. Time for the faint of heart to get out and into a moving boat where they can soak up the scene rather than the effluent. The only thing that can thrive in heavily-polluted water is sewage fungus and that doesn't do anything any good. Sewage fungus is the name given to a complex community of bacteria all of which feed on the organic waste, using up the oxygen dissolved in the water: bad luck for anything else that needs a bit of air. Even worse it blankets green water plants with a clinging slime that shuts out the light and impedes healthy growth. However, at this stage, given time and no further infall of pollution, the river's natural processes will disperse the muck and break down the toxics, recharging the water with oxygen so that other things can live again.

It's raining; the land is watered and the river rises; overflow across the water meadows carries rich mud — a free supply of fertilizer. The whole area is a wonderfully warm and damp, sheltered living place, providing ideal conditions for a wide range of aquatic plants, sedges, reeds, orchids, stoneworts and duckweeds, bulrushes and meadowsweet. The water's edge is propped by dark alder and caressed by drooping willows; and between the branches, swallows and martins glide and dive, wagtails wag, dippers dip and heron wait. And although the water looks very, very muddy, as it drains back down into the river it's naturally filtered and cleansed. Left behind on the meadows are the all-important nutrients. No wonder farmers cashed in on such places, turning them into a chequer-board of productive fields. Otmoor in the upper reaches of the Thames was like this. But recently it has been threatened by a reservoir, a motorway, even a repository for nuclear waste. The real problem, however, is pressure from farming. Hedges and trees that once teemed with flowers, birds, insects and animals have disappeared — replaced by ever-bigger fields and intensive crops. High grain yields can't be produced on water-logged soils, so noisy, gas-guzzling pumps suck the fields dry. Millions of gallons of water a day are removed and with it goes all those free nutrients. The pampered crops need regular attention — fertilizers, pesticides, herbicides — all the latest in farming the modern way, all of which cost the farmer an ever-increasing amount of money.

But who counts the other costs? Without waterlogged soils many already rare plants, like fen violets and marsh orchids will disappear and their cleansing power will be gone. Already across the country, the draining of wetlands like these, added to pollution from a wide variety of sources, has threatened the future of many plants, birds, animals and insects. Four species of dragonfly have been lost from Britain in the last twenty-five years. Insects like these are known indicators of a healthy habitat, a self-purifying river system. Imagine life without the dance of these silver-winged darters, skimmers, hawkers and brilliant emeralds. It may be harder to work up quite the same amount of concern for less dramatic insects like mayfly, caddis fly, diving beetle, alder fly and their larvae. But they are all very sensitive to pollution, and their disappearance from water habitats bodes badly for the rest of the wetland food chain — and that includes all river visitors. For once the predators have been killed, their prey like mosquitoes, midges, and gnats will thrive to the immense irritation of all but themselves.

Britain's fifty-four species of freshwater fish, including perch, pike, roach, eel, trout and grayling, depend upon clean, oxygen-rich, fresh-waters for their health and survival. Take them away and you impair the leisure activity of one of the most formidable lobbies for conservation across the world – the anglers. There are shoals of them, over 3 million in Britain alone, and they are often the first to spot detrimental change to our waterways, the first voices to speak out in support of the fish and hence the wildlife. The angler's legacy is already a diminished one: the UK's natural freshwater fish stocks have been considerably depleted over the last twenty-five years, despite desperate attempts at management and restocking. If your grandfather was a fisherman he'll recall burns and rivers alive with fish. Today you can sit by many a river in Britain or even in the remoter parts of the world, and hardly see a ripple of water.

Anglo-Saxon drainage practices drove the beaver from Britain's rivers . . . and the adoption of post-Second World War industrial agricultural practices including drainage drove the once-common otter from his holt. Water is as essential to wildlife as it is to humans. Together, wildlife and water are the basis for a whole range of human leisure activites, fishing, boating, wildfowling, birdwatching, even tiddler-hunting. Endanger the health of water and its wildlife, and a critical economic, social and aesthetic human resource is also threatened.

So it is, that down the length of the Thames or any other developed river, water is extracted, cleaned when need be, and returned in an altered state to flow its way down to the next intake. 'In out, in out,' shouts the Cox of an Oxford Rowing Eight . . . and in out, in out goes the water, used and abused again and again.

To investigate just one such water cycle we must now bank our boat and take a look at Britain's waterworks and sewage system – the first 'national health service' of the first of the great industrialized nations.

DRAINING OUR SUPPLIES

Everyone flying in to London's Heathrow Airport must have seen the great reservoirs of Thames water and all that it contains, ready to be piped to the city after adequate treatment. In ageing water works, monuments of industrial architecture, natural processes are used to clean the water. In essence it is filtered through beds of clean sand stuffed with microscopic organisms that also get to work and help scrub it clean. Chlorine is then added to kill any remaining germs and off it goes to be pumped and piped potable into our homes. 120 million gallons is treated like this every day in just one of many treatment works. This renders it all sweet and ready for your average First World family of four who use and waste about 300 gallons a day, whether they know it or not. Fresh water from filth, it's a miracle, like water into wine – and clearer than even some of that.

Potable it may be but there are other hidden problems. For a start, this filtered water now contains four times more nitrate than it did when we were children. Both the European Economic Community and the World Health Organization have strict rules about how much nitrate there should be in our drinking water; and many countries in the world are in instant danger of breaking those rules. Two specific problems have been identified; methaemoglobinaemia in human

A watery retreat?

infants – 'the blue-baby' syndrome – and stomach cancer in adults. Too much nitrate in adult diets can cause cancer of the gut. Too much nitrate in the blood of new-born babies prevents their blood supply from transporting oxygen around their bodies. Death is by strangulation – from the inside out. Both conditions are rare, but nitrates are an assured culprit and the existence of international safety levels is an indication of high-level concern. Three main sources contribute to excess nitrate in our water supplies: discharges from sewage works; the use of nitrate fertilizers; and the ploughing up of traditional grasslands, a process which releases large quantities of nitrates that are then carried into the groundwater by rainfall. More people living on a catchment means more nitrate flowing through – and that's as much a fact of life as catching a cold.

However, the most worrying aspect has in recent years been the increased

Opposite

Above *Drainage and pollution of wetlands put the survival of such gems as the kingfisher and bog violet at stake.*

Below *Fenland water meadow. Natural habitats like this filter pollution and breathe oxygen into the water supply – nature's own sewage treatment system.*

'nitrification' caused by intensive modern farming methods. In the last ten years alone, there has been nearly a 50% increase in the use of nitrogen fertilizers by farmers, from 711,200 tonnes of the stuff prior to 1974 to nearly $1\frac{1}{2}$ million tonnes by 1985 in Britain alone. The increased concentration of nitrate in groundwater, its seepage into aquifers and the water table – to be served up eventually through the tap and the kettle onto the tea table, is enough to worry the guests at most tea parties, even those held at Buckingham Palace. There are of course establishments whose proud boast is *'don't worry, all the water used has been passed by the management.'* They probably all live upstream.

The problem has been called the 'Nitrate Time Bomb' as we are yet to feel the full effects of the intense applications of nitrates on the soil over the last ten years. It takes time to seep through – and all eyes are on East Anglia, a sales paradise for nitrogen dealers in the 60s and 70s. They may play down the idea of blue-babies and stomach cancer, but in readiness for the 'Nitrate Bomb', England's water authorities are already investing in complicated and expensive equipment to combat the enemy before it gets to our throats. In the UK alone over $1\frac{1}{2}$ million people are thought to be at risk from nitrate poisoning. So far there have been few cases reported of the blue baby problem. But with rising nitrate levels and with current levels in considerable excess of the 50 milligrams for every litre limit recommended by the EEC, the risk is rapidly becoming unacceptable. When added to the already high levels of lead and aluminium present in the water supply, these represent an indigestible problem – a pollution peril lurking in the kitchen tap. In some parts of Germany where agriculture is intensive, townships are abandoning traditional local water supplies because of fears about nitrate levels: and they're going to great expense to pump supplies from a 'safe distance'. Bottled, nitrate-free water is already common on the continent: it won't be long before it's commonplace in Britain too, delivered daily to the doorstep with the morning milk.

Nitrates are of course not man-made. They are the product of the nitrogen cycle, one of the natural mechanisms by which essential chemicals are exchanged between living things and their environment. They are naturally contained in decaying matter and in small amounts in rivers and lakes where all water plants, including the tiny algae, use them as food. Some more nitrates should be good news. But there can be too much of a good thing, and inorganic fertilizers applied by farmers have upset the balance: the crops don't absorb all that is supplied to them and the excess provides an unexpected free meal for the algae. They reproduce rapidly and overpopulate the river. They float on the surface cutting off the light from underwater plants. These die and decompose, their remains using up the oxygen in the water. In turn this suffocates the fish and other water creatures. The beautiful but deadly 'algal bloom' occurs, and with it a harvest of dead fish lying floating on the surface.

All this is the result of a process called eutrophication, the over-enrichment of water with nitrate and other products that make water plants grow too fast, tipping the balance towards catastrophe. Where it occurs, river and lake water becomes life-less and evil-smelling. The worst-affected area in Britain is the

Norfolk Broads, but many other waterways are in danger, so a constant watch must be kept and purer supplies switched in to defuse the nitrate bomb. Not just in the water but on the river banks too, and wherever water is used for irrigation.

Disposal of human waste starts with a bowel movement, quickly followed by a casual flick of the human hand to trigger about 10 litres of pure water to flush the toilet bowl. From then on it is mixed and diluted with everyone else's on route for the sewage works. Here, hundreds of levers pump compressed air into the water activating millions of bacteria to break down all the organic waste. Yes, the world's sewage works, many built back in the last century, still rely on the natural processes which used to take place back in the river, bacteria breaking down organic matter, using up the oxygen and releasing minerals as they go. It's strange to think that most of us just flush the loo and forget about it. In fact the only time we really think about the local sewage works is when we phone them up to tell them they're smelling too much! Yet we add to the problems all the time; it's not just big industries which pollute. Each one of us plays a part, with our soaps and detergents, bleaches and dyes, multi-coloured toilet paper, hair tints, dead medicines and cigarette ends. Even the DIY empty-your-car-sump enthusiast does his bit. Sewage treatment involves natural processes dependent on living organisms. But any one of those throw-away chemicals can kill these natural processes stone dead and bring the whole thing grinding to a halt.

The more affluent we become the more complex are the effluents of our society. Old sewage works were not designed to handle lead and zinc, let alone the thousands of new chemicals and drugs. In the United States over 10,000 organic chemicals are synthesized, traces of all of which find their way, sooner or later, into rivers, streams, sewage treatment plants and the water supply. Add to these 100,000 man-made chemicals, 5 million chemical compounds and up to 40 million research chemicals, and you've got a very lively – or deadly – mixture. Concern about chemical residues in our water supplies and especially in our drinking water after sewage extraction and treatment led one UK water board, the Thames Water Authority, to introduce new quality control procedures to assess the nature and concentration of some known micro-pollutants. Samples from one tributary of the Thames, the River Lee, which during the drought of 1976 contained almost 60% of effluent from the sewage treatment works, were sufficiently safe for it to be given a reasonably clean bill of health. The levels of pollution discovered were not 'significant'.

We now know that elsewhere in the Thames catchment area, government munitions and atomic weapons research centres and factories have been producing radio-active waste on a daily basis for many years. So far the water authority has resisted requests to allow dangerous radio-active tritium to be mixed and diluted with sewage prior to being discharged into the sea; but their records show that both Burghfield Royal Ordnance Factory and the nuclear research centre at Harwell regularly discharge wastes into Thames tributaries. These wastes are 'not specifically assessed' for toxicity down-river – which seems a curious omission. As Crown organizations, they are exempt from prosecution against any excessive water pollution caused by their activities. In 1985, independent researchers

discovered radio-active plutonium, uranium and tritium from these plants flowing directly through waste pipes into the Thames ... indirectly into the capital's water supply. Water and sewage treatment processes cannot cope with radio-activity, it escapes all the filters, all the known safety nets. Both plants have been in existence for many years and presumably have been officially disposing of radio-active poisons into taps and kettles throughout London for the same period.

We are constantly regaled with the fact that salmon are once again swimming up the Thames. This was impossible for many years due to the organic load in the water which used up all the oxygen (a process aptly termed BOD – Biological Oxygen Demand). The river is now clearer thanks to the trojan work of the Thames Water Authority. The sewage sludge, complete with more than its fair share of all the other products of our effluent society are taken by barge and dumped for better or worse into the North Sea. Yet staff at the major sewage works are worried that if large amounts of money are not spent now to rebuild and update the works, the clocks could be rapidly turned back in a rather foul way. If you thought that out-of-date or decrepit sewage treatment works were a problem, how about the sewer pipes? These form a national network stretching across town and country and down and under Britain's great industrial towns. There's 240,000 kilometres of them – ninety times the length of all Britain's motorways.

Northumbrian Water's model sewage treatment works in Tyneside – elsewhere the UK sewage system is literally crumbling.

A quarter of these were built during Victorian times, over eighty years ago; and it was Victorian affluence which did so much to devise a system which would make Britain's towns and cities cleaner and healthier.

But many are now falling into disrepair, and some are collapsing. Between 1982 and 1985 there were over 11,000 'significant sewer collapses' and blockages in England where stretches of effluent-blocked tunnel had to be re-excavated and shored up. The roots of some mighty trees have even found their way into the tunnel network, creating havoc amidst the masonry and warning us that whatever we do, nature moves on regardless. The same is true for the sewage. If it can't move on down these Victorian Roads to the sewage works, it will seep out into the foundations of the local real estate. The decay and collapse of sewage infra-structures is a problem found across the urban world. Without costly programmes of renovation and renewal, the lifestyles of the urban industrial world could soon descend to the level of the open sewer.

It's advisable to don protective clothing for our next detour, to the River Mersey. One look at the sewage system and you can see why!

Here is one of the very worst of Britain's open sewers − the River Mersey in Liverpool, home of the Beatles and a once-great industrial trading port which, like the sewers, has gone completely to the dogs. The ferry across the Mersey traverses one of the filthiest stretches of water in the world.

Fifty horrible orifices − the end of the road for some of the collapsing sewers of this decaying city − pour untreated waste from over 1 million people into the Mersey Estuary − the mouth of a river system which rises in the landscapes of the High Pennines, the 'Backbone of Britain'. Many contemporary Liverpudlians remember swimming in the Mersey as children, it was so clean. Now it's known locally as the 'typhoid dip'. If you fall in accidentally, you are whipped off to hospital to have your stomach pumped, . . . and the contents plus all the other hospital effluent go back into the river! The whole Mersey area contains a third of Britain's most polluted rivers and canals, the effluents from which all flow on down towards the sea.

We follow the current and the path of the effluent down to the coast, dropping in on a few seaside 'resorts'.

Estuaries swept clean by sweet water are ideal places for industry and for ports. Yet estuarine pollution is a problem across the globe, from the Tees to the Rhine, from the Mersey to East Bengal. Periodically it takes its toll on the wildlife populations of the flats, shallows and banks, where seals and fish come to breed, where shellfish feed on the bountiful microscopic flora and fauna, and where birds who need a port of call stop on their long migratory flights. It is amazing how much wildlife actually can co-exist with industry if only given a chance. The fact is that they rarely are; and although they will avoid the most badly polluted areas, there is little they can do in the event of a sudden flush of chemical poisons, like in

The Rhine near Bonn – a great river system for transport – and industrial effluent.

1980 on the Mersey Estuary, when 2500 dunlin, redshank, curlew, duck and black-headed gull were all found dead one morning at low tide. The cause of this massacre was organic lead – the petrol additive that has led to tremendous public outcry. The pollution continues, however. Do we have to wait for another catastrophe? Next time it could be 2500 children.

All the Mersey river and estuarine pollution ends up in the Irish Sea. But a lot gets washed along the sands of the local seaside towns. New Brighton Beach in Merseyside, a natural amenity used by thousands of people throughout the summer, is Britain's most polluted holiday resort. In Victorian times, it attracted 4 million holidaymakers every year. It had a fine pier, clean bathing beaches, a huge tower and a ferry. Today the ferry sails no longer, the tower and the pier are long gone, half the town centre is boarded up, and the water edge is awash with faeces, contraceptives, toiletries, household waste and sewer scum. In the public toilets on the promenade there are notices which proclaim 'now wash your hands'. But there's no warning about swimming in what is no more than dilute sewage – and other people's into the bargain.

Similar stories can be told all over Europe, so the EEC has introduced a directive requiring European beaches to observe a common standard of water quality for bathers. To be designated a safe 'Eurobeach', 100 millilitres of bathing water should not contain more than 10,000 coliform bacteria, or 2000 faecal bacteria. Some authorities say that even this standard is too lax, yet in Britain only twenty-seven beaches across the country complied – were clean

enough for designation. The UK's beaches receive the contents of some 460
sewage outfalls, over half of which discharge totally untreated sewage. Some of
the most dangerous beaches are also those most popular with holidaymakers . . .
those at Scarborough, Great Yarmouth, Brighton and Blackpool. With statistics
like this to swim in it is little wonder that every year one million holidaymakers
flock abroad. But are foreign and European beaches any cleaner? France and Spain
list thousands of Eurobeaches between them. But some of these lie between
coastal areas which have very high levels of localized contamination. According to
the Organization for Economic Co-operation and Development, some coastal
stretches which are very popular with holidaymakers are at the extreme limit of
acceptable pollution; like those around Valencia, Barcelona, Athens, Marseilles,
the Northern parts of the Tyrrhenian and Adriatic Seas, San Francisco Bay and
many others. This international body cynically observed that in many of these
areas 'bathing ought to be prohibited, but in fact is not for reasons of reputation
and the local economy'.

Out at sea, dumped sewage wastes, sludge and coastal effluent, much of which
is non bio-degradable, is accumulating at depth and shifting around with the
tides, endangering biological balances among fish-stocks, vegetation and
invertebrates. The effect of known poisons like aldrin, dieldrin, mercury, PCBs
and titanium dioxide on fish is well known: North Sea catches now regularly
include fish with ulcers and a range of cancerous growths. The Mediterranean is a
virtually enclosed sea with no real tides; it takes seventy years to renew its waters,

The last resort?

yet is at the receiving end of the industrial and domestic pollution of some seventeen nations sharing a common coastline. To this must be added the pollution caused by the pressure of over 100 million tourists every year, most of them seeking safe bathing in that salty cess-pit. The pollution of the Med is an old problem: the Romans used to complain of its filthy beaches and took their holidays instead on the Atlantic coast of Spain. Even Leonardo Da Vinci suggested that a model of the Mediterranean should be made to check on its levels of pollution.

Europe is indeed fortunate that to date nothing catastrophic has happened, and that the recent reduction in fish catches of her most productive seas are due to overfishing, taking too much out rather than putting too much in. There's no getting away from the fact that a very important part of the marine resources is their ability to receive our many wastes. But for how long can we continue to push the limits? Our seas do have a cleansing and recycling ability to accept and deal with a certain amount of our waste but only if given the chance to put pure water back into circulation. The laws of evaporation have not changed: the salts are left behind, and pure sweet water goes up on its way. But not for long: people pressure is also polluting the water cycle while the water vapour is still up in the air.

Our journey round the water cycle takes us up into the atmosphere, to see what the problems are up there.

Every year the world's fossil fuels power stations pump millions of tonnes of sulphur dioxide up into the atmosphere to add to that from domestic and natural sources. Dissolved in the embryonic rain, this becomes dilute sulphuric acid. In Europe, Britain emits more than her fair share. Some $2\frac{1}{2}$ million tonnes of the stuff earn Britain the acronym EDM – Europe's Dirty Man. Every year petrol engines belch out oxides of nitrogen helping to form the notorious acid rain. There is no doubt that these acids are eating away not only at our lungs, but at the facades of all our buildings – corroding and eroding everything from 13th-century stained glass to the Empire State Building and everything in between. Strident voices are now blaming acid rain for all sorts of atrocities, like the widespread death of forest trees and whole lake and river systems. The argument is that acid water mobilizes aluminium, mercury, cadmium, lead, zinc, magnesium and many other toxic substances that are present in the soil, and moves them into rivers and lakes where they act as toxins, wreaking havoc amongst the fish and other aquatic life. At first sight, it seems unlikely in open-flow, self-cleaning systems. However only one peak dose is needed, and the damage is done.

Acid emissions which enter the water cycle don't just precipitate in the form of rain: they can also take the form of mist or fog, like the London smogs of the last century. The effect is just as deadly and the occurrence itself can be dramatic: in 1984 scientists recorded a precipitation of black snow in the Cairngorm mountains of northern Scotland. The fall was slight, only five centimetres, but the acid content was high, and over the weeks it commingled with the more plentiful white snow to form a distinctive grey layer in the snowpack – some 40 centimetres thick . . . concentrated poison ready for the spring.

Frost action also aids the release of a whole range of minerals in the soil. The acid snow-melt flushes, then releases the whole lot into the river, hitting the fish at their most vulnerable post-winter crisis stage. The casualty list appears to be mounting: 90% of Sweden's lakes are acidified and some 4000 have entirely lost their fish stocks. In Norway, a survey showed that 1711 lakes (over 60%) had lost their fish due to acidification. In Ontario, Canada, an estimated 48,000 lakes are threatened with extinction. Once fish-filled lakes in south-west Cumbria, the Galloway area of Scotland and the Llyn Brianne area of Wales, have become very near fish-less as acid depositions have increased over the years. In 1938, 1406 brown trout were fished from the waters of Loch Grannoch in Scotland; by 1960, the catch was down to 620, by 1964 it was 45, by 1975 it was three. In 1980 there were none. The once pure water of Loch Grannoch had become like diluted vinegar. The water looks clean. From the surface you can see the moss on the floor. The clarity is crystal. But it is the clarity of death, of acid death.

Loch Grannoch's clarity tells any hydrobiologist that it is an oligotrophic lake – characterized by low production because its waters originate amongst hard rocks which weather slowly and release little in the way of plant nutrients. So it has never had great rejuvenating resources . . . it doesn't take much to tip the balance. The lake shores are flanked with forests, some natural, others planted with conifers – more recent plantations of exotic species. Both – the exotics especially – need acid soils and release acid into the environment.

Above the forest, overgrazing by sheep, moor burning and artificial drainage destroy the acid peat blanket, acidifying the waters which drain into the Loch. All these factors tip a fine acid balance into acid overkill.

Changing land-use patterns have a lot to answer for. Much of the land on which the industrial nations of the North now live was still under the glaciers of the last ice age only 15,000 years ago. Ice action rejuvenated the landscapes, releasing mineral nutrients and the bases which could buffer any acidity. Great natural mixed forests developed on rich soils kept naturally sweet by the annual fall of leaves. Now afforestation takes all and puts nothing back – except a few tough old acidic pine needles.

In the 1960s it was impossible to grow good trees in England's South Pennines because of acidic emissions from the power stations of south-east Lancashire and domestic fires. Then the Clean Air Act began to work and the Central Electricity Generating Board introduced its 'high stack' policy to carry acid wastes higher into the atmosphere. As a result, tree-growth in the South Pennines has markedly improved. The local effect has been reduced . . . But the emissions themselves are simply landing further afield on other peoples' doorsteps. The higher the smokestack the further it goes.

Controlling acid rain is expensive. The introduction of flue scrubbers in power stations could add to the cost of generating electricity. The liming of hills and lakes to restore alkalinity is an expensive, and at best only a temporary solution.

But these pale into insignificance against the environmental costs, the build-up of danger to human and animal health, and the direct economic consequences on impaired fisheries and food production (agriculture in Britain is thought to have lost over £200 million as a result of acidification) and depleted rural resources for leisure and tourism. In actual fact no-one really knows or is able to accurately estimate the true environmental dangers and economic costs of acid rain. In the UK the authorities say that the environmentalists are demanding a 'billion dollar solution to a million dollar problem'. The costs, and indeed even the causes, of acid rain are widely disputed and there is a clear need for more research. Meanwhile the problem is not getting better.

Acid rain increases the attraction for some of nuclear power as an alternative to fossil-fuels, hence the joke slogan: acid rain causes nuclear power. In fact that would intensify the water pollution problem – endangering the health of not just lakes and rivers but the great home of all water, fresh, clean or polluted – the sea itself.

Back to sea level, we move up the coastlines of the world and far out into the open sea. Here a storm of problems is gathering ready to roll in on the shore, and threatening more than just the quality of our water supplies.

If we humans use the sky as a waste-flue, we use the depths of the world's oceans as a chamber pot, as the final dumping ground for all the excrescence of civilization – particularly those things we don't want to see again, like nuclear waste, toxic, outdated weaponry, and human effluent. We can thank our lucky stars that the sea can deal with human excreta in its 'purest' form, but as to what happens when we mix in all those other man-made wastes and concentrated long-living toxics, we can only guess.

The littoral, the place where sea meets land, is a harsh environment, but supports some of the most diverse living communities on the face of the globe. From the richness of tropical coral reef to the magnificence of temperate kelp forest, each zoned seaweed garden is a flourishing genetic reservoir, sporting the full armamentarium of evolution from simple unicells to the most complex of life forms. Each finds its place in the watery web of life.

The sea contains infinitely delicate chemical balances involving a wide range of natural elements, present in key proportions to one another. Without strontium, molybdenum and titanium present in balanced quantities, seaweeds would not flourish. Without chromium, zinc and potassium in precise numbers of parts per 1000 million of water, fish tissue would not function properly. The chemical balance in the sea supports a harvest of microscopic plants and animals. These are plankton, and there are over 50,000 to every cupful of sea-water. These are the meadows which feed shellfish, the food storehouses of the great whales, the pastures of the deep which support a diverse and productive chain of life. The sea holds both the secrets of the origin of life and our hopes for the future. Yet we appear to be doing everything in our power to turn large parts of it into toxic soup.

Singeing in the rain! German spruce forest under assault by over-acidity.

Just up the English west coast from the Mersey Estuary in the beautiful county of Cumbria, home of hosts of golden daffodils and one of the world's great heritage landscapes, the English Lakes, lies the Sellafield nuclear power and re-processing complex. Every working day of its radio-active half-life this plant emits radio-active water through waste-pipes deep into the Irish Sea and vents through flues radio-active gases into the atmosphere above it. These are all 'permissible' emissions which we are told constitute 'No Immediate Danger' to the public or threat to the environment, even though they contain traces (and at times 'leaked' volumes) of plutonium, tritium and caesium. 'Low level' and 'no danger' maybe, but they are long-lived, toxic and cumulative. Ironically, some of the chemical processes involved at Sellafield require water of the freshest quality and the highest purity. This most poisonous plant in Europe and, possibly the world, consumes crystal-clear water from some of the purest of all freshwater reservoirs – the tarns, streams and lakes of the Lake District. It sucks in crystal purity and pipes out radioactive poison. Discharged into the sea, Sellafield's toxic wastes are brought back on shore by the tide, polluting beaches, contaminating shellfish and bird life and endangering the human community. One substance

Greenpeace dinghy testing the radio-active pollution in the Irish Sea, near Sellafield.

which is discharged in large quantities is plutonium 241. In the short space of fourteen years, this decays into a highly toxic substance which is washed up on the shoreline or carried by currents across the sea to the Isle of Man and the Irish coast. A possible correlation between a high incidence of leukaemia in young children and radio-active emissions here and at other nuclear establishments in the UK is currently being investigated. One possible effect on wildlife can already be seen. Five years ago, the Ravenglass Estuary Dunes, close to the Sellafield pipeline and the leaking nuclear fuel dump at Drigg, sported a thriving colony of 16,000 pairs of nesting black-headed gulls. The colony had been there since before human times, and was mentioned in the Domesday Book. It was one of the biggest colonies of its kind in Britain. But in 1985 it was suddenly and mysteriously abandoned. Like the ravens of the Tower of London, deserting their perches when disaster threatened, the birds of Ravenglass had flown.

They used to breed at high water mark where concentrates of waste plutonium from Sellafield are found. But in recent times the gulls had been unable to rear any young: eggs did not hatch, chicks did not feed and died within a few days. Over the years the birds had moved further and further away from the Sellafield Works, until, reaching the far edge of their colony, they gave it up completely. Their apparent distaste for a radio-active diet and atmosphere is shared by other bird species, such as widgeon, teal, arctic and sandwich terns and oystercatcher. These have either abandoned the area altogether or seen their numbers severely reduced.

Official dogma blames human disturbance and increased predation by feral fox and mink. But this would not explain the birds' inability to hatch their eggs. To date there is no proof that emissions from Sellafield are the culprit in emptying the skies and seas around Seascale of its birds. But radiation works in mysterious ways, and we know where we would put our bets. Is this nature's way of telling us something's wrong? Birds have always been the miner's lamp on pollution. Caged canaries were carried into the pits to warn the miners about the presence of gas pockets underground. A canary that stopped singing was a sure sign of trouble ahead. And the deaths of large numbers of birds blew the cover on DDT. Is the black-headed gull blowing the cover on Sellafield-Windscale? Scientists do not as yet fully understand what happens when radiation enters the food chain. But an informed local joke in Cumbria tells of herring gulls dropping plutonium bombs on the populace.

The Irish Sea into which Sellafield still pours its deadly effluent is recognized by environmental officials as the most radio-active sea in the world. Probably the next most radio-active is part of the greatest ocean of all, the South Pacific.

This is the final destination on our journey through the water cycle. And it's no dream holiday to paradise, but a nuclear nightmare.

Located at the very centre of the watery half of the globe, the South Pacific includes some twenty-two island states spread over an area equivalent to the size of Africa. All these islands, and the warm sea around them add up to one of the most productive, and as yet relatively unexploited regions of the earth. Yet the whole area is currently being subjected to a long list of environmental pressures. None of these is more sinister than that of pollution from radiation. There is a long and ignoble history of nuclear weapons testing in the area by foreign powers, including the British, the Soviets, and the Americans. By the time these powers had withdrawn in 1963, the Americans alone had tested at least 103 nuclear bombs in the region.

After one hydrogen bomb test at the Bikini-Eniwetok Atoll area in 1954, the islanders of neighbouring Rongelap Atoll were caught downwind of the blast. The children were at first stunned by the blinding flash and the shock wave, but later they played excitedly with the 'snow' – over three inches of deadly radio-active fall-out. Many suffered radiation burns, and nineteen out of the twenty-nine children under ten at the time have developed thyroid growths. Some died of leukaemia. Native women talk in horror of giving birth to 'human jellyfish' – babies born dead without limbs and bones. The other legacy of this snowstorm in paradise was the poisoning of the deep, the main food storehouse of all Polynesians. Ciguatera poisoning may be officially a natural phenomena related to fish-eating toxic plankton, but why is it that when American scientists visit Rongelap every year to do atmospheric tests on radiation pollution, they bring their own food rather than eat the choice lobsters, the turtles or the giant clams offered to them by the islanders?

Since the 1960s the French have been testing regularly, focusing their experiments on the area around Muroroa Atoll. There have been 130 separate detonations in nineteen years; sixty have been overground. Both overground and underground explosions have been accompanied by widespread radio-active contamination through the dispersal of fall-out, radio-active leakage and seepage and through the casual dumping of weapons and laboratory waste. The lagoon at Muroroa, the recipient of hundreds of thousands of metric tons of radio-active waste, is now a seeping tank of plutonium poisons. And the Atoll itself is breaking up, fracturing under the assult of the regular explosions. Obsessed with continued testing and re-testing of atomic processes, the deadly efficiency of which the world can be in no doubt, the French carry on. They heedlessly disregard world opinion, the direct contamination of fish, plankton and coral reef, and the high incidence of still-births and thyroid cancers among the native people of the surrounding Polynesian islands.

To date there is a virtual absence of any scientific assessment of the complete environmental impact of radio-active pollution on the flora, fauna and human life of the South Pacific. But even if that were done efficiently and objectively, it would only be a partial measure. Because of the particularly insidious, gene-damaging nature of radiation, the true effects, the true impact of this oceanic tragedy, will probably not be revealed for generations to come. Just like Raveng-lass, no birds fly over Muroroa. These once glamorous, palm-fringed seascapes, have become places of the apocalypse. The tale of the Walrus and the Carpenter, from Lewis Carroll's *Alice Through the Looking Glass*, now assumes a monstrously foreboding character.

Fishing in Micronesia. But with evidence of irradiated clams and toxic plankton – would you buy fish from this haul?

'The sea was wet as wet could be, the sands were dry as dry.
You could not see a cloud, because no cloud was in the sky:
No birds were flying overhead – there were no birds to fly.'

If they could walk *these* sands, the walrus and the carpenter would indeed shed many a bitter tear.

Whatever the vested interests say, Muroroa and Ravenglass do not present a fit legacy for the future world of our children. But some people have been making waves against this particular tide of desecration, this sea of seeping radio-active poison. One remarkable environmental pressure group, Greenpeace, is particularly concerned with man's destruction of the ocean, and has successfuly spilled the beans at both Sellafield and Muroroa. The British establishment responded to their 'unlawful' actions with prosecution and an enormous fine. The French responded by sinking their ship *Rainbow Warrior*, causing the death of crew member Fernando Pereira. The public outcry and the wave of anti-nuclear feeling that followed each incident has simply further undermined the public position and credibility of the international nuclear military-industrial club.

Marked by the death of a rainbow, our tour of the water cycle is complete. Having considered the dilution and the pollution, we move aside now, ahead of supply, to consider a few clean-water points, some of the solutions.

CLEANING UP THE WATERCOURSES

The defiant actions of groups like Greenpeace, and the warm public support they are beginning to receive, mark the turning of the tide for the water polluters. Perhaps in this environmental issue more than any other, the true consequences of our actions have hit right home and touched our hearts. Water is a sacred, purifying substance in cultures across the globe; we are sentimental about our rivers and our seas. In these terms, their destruction and desecration is not just suicidal, it's an act of sacrilege against life itself. Still waters run deep: remember the reaction of one of the heroes in *Wind in the Willows* when he first caught sight of the gurgling, chuckling river:

'The mole was bewitched, entranced, fascinated. By the side of the river he trotted as one trots, when very small, by the side of a man, who holds one spellbound by exciting stories; and when tired at last, he sat on the bank, while the river still chattered on to him, a babbling procession of the best stories in the world, sent from the heart of the earth to be told at last to the insatiable sea.'

The *Wind in the Willows* is just a story, but it is based on the real River Pang in Berkshire. Sir Richard Body, chairman of an association of small farmers and a British Member of Parliament lives there. The destruction of the river by drainage authorities and agricultural ministries, has inspired him to campaign vigorously against their lunatic excesses. He wrote an epitaph for the Pang:

'First the trees were felled. Then came the dredgers to straighten some of the bends and lower the water table to make stretches of it look more like a scaled-down version of the Grand Union Canal than a meandering chalk stream.

Lowering the water table is necessary because arable crops, like wheat, barley and oil seed rape, cannot grow unless the wet lowland is dried out by drainage; and in the valley, the larger farmers have been goaded by grants; subsidies and import levies into growing such crops, instead of keeping cattle and sheep. A few of us with smallholdings continue to breed and fatten cattle, and three have dairy herds; and we need a high water table to enable the grass to grow well all through the dry summer months. Also the great variety of grasses and flora that make our cattle fatten into top quality meat cannot flourish on dried out land. Some of the flora has died out and disappeared; and the beef is the poorer for it. Beef from these fields has been, according to the wholesale butchers, the best in a radius of many miles. Our interests are thus, by public policy, put in conflict with those of the other farmers. Some of the wild flowers have gone, others are markedly fewer. Of the birds, the snipe, the peewit and the kingfisher are seen no more and the mallard and the moorhen are many fewer. Removal of the cover along the river bank has taken away the habitat of the otter and the water vole – 'Ratty' of *Wind in the Willows*.'[10]

The ripples caused by the actions of respectable establishment figures like Body and others have spread widely and drawn many other organization into the pool of discontent. Things are changing. Here are some of their positive goals which would go a fair way to turning the tide.

- Tighter controls on river and coastal pollution by public works and the private sector; enforcement of the 'polluter pays' principle on all bodies, public and private

- Introduction of a private tax on the use of nitrogen to offset the public cost of de-nitrification

- Incentives for organic farming to replace chemical farming, to reduce excessively high levels of nitrogen which go into the soil

- A system of pollution monitors or wardens, voluntary or part-time water keepers and 'coast-guards', to monitor effluent emissions in rivers, lakes and coasts

- The acceleration of all river and water clean-up campaigns

- More freedom of information about industrial and chemical processes which pollute land, water and air, and which end up being transported around in our water supply

- Legislation requiring that waste control and pollution management be made part of all industrial profit and loss accounts, particularly in the nuclear, farming and chemical industries

- Incentives for manufacturing industries to convert to 'water-sympathetic' production techniques, using water-degradable materials and processes, and the manufacture of bio-degradable products

- Colour-coding in all manufactured liquids to indicate their level of bio-degradability in water

- Modernization of sewage systems and the re-building of sewage tunnel networks under our towns, cities and districts

- Prohibition of the pollution of any water anywhere with untreated human sewage

- Pressure on energy industries to use available technology for reducing sulphur emissions from fossil-fuelled power stations

- The adoption by car manufacturers of lean-burn car technology to reduce nitrous oxide emissions, to reduce acid levels in the water supply and save precious fuel

- A moratorium on all future development of the nuclear industry and of nuclear fuel processing, at least until a way is found of safely disposing of radio-active wastes

- A complete ban on all nuclear weapons-testing in marine or any other areas

- The establishment of independent water-monitoring bodies to monitor the efficiency of pollution control measures – water quality control teams separate from water suppliers and polluters

- Tighter controls on estuarine pollution and establishment of estuary boards to monitor further clean-up

- More careful monitoring of all manufacturing processes that produce effluents contained in the infamous 'Black List' established by the Oslo and Paris Conventions and EEC Directives

- The establishment by governments of an international water commission to enforce international legislation on oil spills and waste dumping, and to ensure the payment of clean-up compensation by all those who break the rules

- More marine nature reserves especially in particularly sensitive coastal habitats

In the developed world generally, the management of local and national water systems is the responsibility of a bewildering array of boards, authorities and councils. These utilities can be public or private sector, or a combination of the two. They usually incorporate the functions of water supply, water treatment, sewage and pollution control and are regulated by an even more bewildering array of legislation and health controls. Their task is vast and their funding is secured by rates and taxes levied on water users: enough, you might think, to manage the water, renew sewage stock and initiate a massive clean-up of rivers and streams.

The UK has shown it can be done in some rivers like the Thames which now have fish, plankton, and life in many estuarine habitats where before there was just rotting pollution. But no UK water authority has been allocated the resources and powers, or one might think, has had the incentive, to implement Section 46 of the 1974 Control of Pollution Act requiring them to bring to an end 'pollution injurious to the fauna and flora of a stream of water'. Nationally, there has been an improvement in river pollution since 1974. But rapid progress is not helped by the fact that the water authorities themselves are the biggest polluters, largely because of the crumbling and inadequate sewage systems they are saddled with propping-up.

In the United Nations Water Decade, 1981–91, the UK, like much of the developed world, should be forced to put its own latrines in order instead of just peddling its expensive hi-tech water supply and treatment technology to Third-World markets. If we have the technology for sustainable water management and sanitization, let's make sure it is applied at home as well as abroad.

Out at sea there also float a bewildering array of international conventions, commissions and assemblies which have drawn up agreements on the control of pollution and the resources of the seas. But water and the oceans still lack a basic universal charter, protecting these international resources from the worst excesses of human greed and pollution. The UN treaty of the 'Third Law of the Sea' is as yet unsigned by leading maritime nations, including the US, the UK and West Germany. This treaty embraces controls and standards on the exploitation of fisheries, of the resources of continental shelves and the deep sea bed, on scientific research and on pollution. If there is ever to be a truly new meaning and purpose to the traditional concept of 'freedom of the seas', a freedom which sustains, not destroys the sea, then this treaty must be signed and ratified as soon as possible.

Regionally, the situation is more hopeful. The UN Environmental Programme initiated in 1974 a regional sea 'clean-up' supported by twenty-six international organizations and 120 nations. Ten clean-ups are under way, the most successful of which is the Mediterranean Action Plan of 1976. Seventeen nations agreed to set aside their differences to tackle the waste which was eating away at their common maritime frontier. Two lists of toxic substances were drawn up: a 'black' list of banned highly toxic wastes; and a 'grey' list of substances requiring controlled discharge. A centre to co-ordinate pollution monitoring by over eighty Mediterranean marine laboratories was established, and plans were drawn up to deal with sewage, agricultural and industrial waste on an international scale. And fifteen marine reserves have been designated in addition to protective measures for endangered Mediterranean species like marine turtles and monk seals. The Mediterranean clean-up is a good example of international co-operation and integrated management in action. If enthusiasm, committment and investment is sustained, the rewards at the end of the day will be tangible: a cleaner sea and beaches, thriving fisheries, more tourist appeal and a resource protected for future generations.

But one marine project which has gone further than this, by devising an actual strategy for integrated sustainable management of a sea eco-system is the Great

Barrier Reef Marine Park. The largest system of coral reefs in the world, with over 2500 reefs, cays and islands stretched across the north-east continental shelf of Australia, the Barrier Reef, supports the most diverse eco-system on the face of the earth, including 1500 species of fish, 400 corals and 4000 species of mollusc. It's a down-under gene-rich paradise, and a critical resource for scientific knowledge, genetic material, fishing and tourism. It is also threatened by pollution, silting, tourist pressure and growing ecological imbalances, like the sudden abundance of formidable coral-eating, crown-of-thorns starfish.

But an authority has been established to control exploitation, regulate development, minimize tourist concentration in sensitive areas, conserve reefs with zoning plans, manage visitors, undertake research, monitor pressure on the reef eco-system and manage the resources accordingly. The 'clean-up' of the reef is at an early stage. But the plans are laid for a shining example of what can and should be done in world water through combining the principles of conservation and development. If sustainable use of a marine resource can be achieved here then there is no barrier to success elsewhere, to a clean and safe turning of the tide of pollution and destruction. Yet the Queensland Government still allows the destruction of unique coastal tropical rainforest, spilling silt and soil and hence death and destruction into this world heritage site, so we must not be complacent.

The water cycle knows no bounds. It affects all of us and we affect all of it: yet in our journey from the clouds in the sky to the great reefs down under, there have been problems all the way. The worst of these are time-bombs for ourselves and our water supply, the nitrates, pesticides, herbicides, heavy-metals and radio-active substances. To stop the excessive flow of these into our world water systems we need urgent local, national and international action and investment. The other problems are being dealt with to an extent, but there progress is too slow. We are told 'these things take time'. But we will have to move more quickly for the one thing we haven't got, in the case of world water, is time.

5 THE GREAT GENE ROBBERY

ACROSS THE GENE SEA

All our pasts, presents and futures are contained in our genes. This is as true for ourselves as it is for the world's great ecosystems: the seas, forests and great wilderness areas. Yet for centuries we have been remorselessly plundering the natural gene banks of the world and systematically destroying the genetic diversity upon which all our futures ultimately depend.

We visit a library and look at some of the acts of piracy which have been perpetrated on the open expanse of the genetic ocean. We take a voyage of re-discovery through the tropical rainforests of the world to the highlands of Peru, where the Conquistadores first came across the humble potato. Returning to shore, we take some bearings from the green ladies of Garhwal in the High Himalayas and from some good old English country gardeners.

We're all banking on the profits of a bright green genetic future inheritance. But are we entrusting our investments with the right sort of banks? Is it time we put our accounts in order?

DIVERSITY IS THE SPICE OF LIFE

Our first port of call is a library, located at the heart of our own personalities, and visible through the deep, searching lenses of an electron microscope.

Switch on the microscope and the picture on the 'micro-page' gives you access to a chromosome 99.9% like one of your own chromosomes. This is part of a forty-six-stack library containing all the information necessary to make a member of the human species, *Homo sapiens*. It also contains 98% of all the information which makes a chimpanzee, *Pongo pygmaeus*.

Your chromosomes – and you have forty-six inside each one of your body cells – are a living compendium of biological history shaped by evolution and donated by your forbears to serve you well throughout one life-time and with some adjustment, to be passed on to your progeny. If you are a little peeved at the stereotyped nature of your genetic inheritance, take consolation in the fact that the total library is so extensive that the other 0.1% of difference is sufficient to make brilliant, scintillating you exactly what you are, complete with all your faults. Wouldn't it then be marvellous if we could reach into that library and by simply extracting snippets of that information breed a perfect person. Someone with the looks of Garbo or Newman, the brains of Einstein and the talents . . . well you know what *you* crave for! The trouble is that everyone would want to get in on the act of perfection and we'd soon get bored with the resulting uniformity. Diversity is the spice of life, and if no one ever grumbled about the President or the cuisine again, nothing could ever be improved.

Of course genetic selection has been happening for centuries as people have bred plants and animals for various purposes, as crops, high milk-yielders, good egg-layers, pure blood-stock and of course pets. The various breeding programmes amplify snippets of unseen genetic information to produce the desired traits. Such breeding has always been fraught with the problems of runts, throw-backs, genetic abnormality, susceptibility to disease and to infertility.

Masai warriors – with their lands and traditional ways of life under threat, how long will they be able to contribute to the genetic diversity of humankind?

Likewise they have taken a long time and have always been very haphazard: you threw the genetic dice and took your chance with the result. But new techniques are beginning to change all that and are speeding up the whole process.

Genetic engineers using all the knowledge and sophisticated gear of their science are now able to reach into those genetic libraries, selecting, moving and reshaping bits of the contained information in an attempt to improve the product. They are building bridges into a new future – a Brave New World in which there could be much less disease, a world without the obscenities of factory-farming and experiments on live animals, a productive, self-sustaining world with less of the tensions and misery created by want, and the economic problems which often lead to war.

Black Rhinoceros – species with an overcast future.

At least this is the dream of some behind the work of this new breed of high-bio-tech scientists. And there are already tangible breakthroughs. Improved yeasts and bacteria have been engineered to synthesize more alcohol. More desirable chemicals have been produced through engineering other microbes, including a whole new spectrum of antibiotics and even interferon which could cure cancer. There is a promise of beans bouncing with animal amino-acids, of crops with built-in nitrogen-fixing capabilities, of petunias which don't feel lonely in onion patches, and much, much more of everything. It really does look as if the genetic and biological engineers hold the promise of creation in their high-tech hands. The cost of doing all this is of course enormous, but the potential prizes are measured in mega-Nobels.

It is therefore little wonder that many people worry that the dream will turn into the reality of an uncontrollable nightmare, with criminal negligence cutting corners, genetic espionage, the worst malpractices of corporate monopoly, and even biological warfare, all in the name of human welfare. Yes, the way ahead is fraught with all sorts of moral, environmental and political problems. Many of these are as novel and as lethal as any of the new bacteria, viruses, insects or even super-crops which could be unleashed onto a world that hasn't got the gene base with which to exercise the necessary control. The challenge, however, is immense. With an estimated 6 billion people to feed and service by the end of the century we cannot afford to close off these new options.

We are, however, closing them off every day, for at the moment, the world is hell-bent on its own form of genetic engineering on a major scale. We are destroying whole genetic libraries, lock and stock, and putting the librarians out of business. This particular game is called extinction, and much of it is happening in the name of progress. The list of plant and animal casualties, of entire species, and of whole-world gene pools that have gone to the wall could fill many a museum, a whole menagerie of extinction. It's that list which makes our future tasks, our attempts to engineer a genetically diverse stable future a daunting prospect.

A quick look inside this menagerie of shame will bring us face to face with some old friends, made famous by the fact that they are no longer there.

The dodo was extinguished in the 1860s by the spread of western 'civilization'. The last great auk was killed in Ireland in 1884, fair game to 'brave' hunters, because it couldn't fly. The remarkable quagar, half-horse, half-zebra, disappeared from the plains of Africa in 1883. The poor old passenger pigeon which once filled the skies and the pies of North America in its millions, was down to one and then none in 1914; followed by the ill-fated Carolina parakeet. And in 1933, (the year which saw the first public appearance of *Homo sapiens* var. David Bellamy, Botanist) the last Tasmanian Wolf died behind bars in a zoo at Hobart. All these unique creatures and countless others have been swept off the face of the earth, often because of the greed and stupidity of humankind.

The process continues: there are hundreds of creatures on the danger list,

*The dodo – extinguished by
adventurers with no eye for the
future.*

threatened with extinction, and about many of them we know remarkably little.
There are many thousands more about which we know nothing at all – they don't
even have a name. The world's list of endangered species includes exotic fairy-tale
creatures like the glorious jaguar, the Siberian tiger, the black and white rhinos,
the blue whale, and many less exotic but just as important types of plant, animal
and lowly insect. There has always been extinction. Since the beginning of life on
earth, over $3\frac{1}{2}$ billion years ago, more than 90% of all species that have existed
have gone to the wall. That's a pretty impressive drop-out rate – one species for
every thousand years – but it was all wholly natural.

But people have moved in and accelerated the process, to the extent that
between 1600 and 1900 over seventy-five species disappeared. And that's just the
mammals and birds we know about. The total number of plants, fishes, reptiles,
amphibians and invertebrates whose candles of existence had also flickered out
probably exceeds that by a hundred-fold. No-one really knows and no-one dares
to make a guess. During the course of the present century we have quickened the
pace, pushing out another seventy-five species of birds and mammals, and
countless plants and other organisms. Today the pace of destruction and extinction goes on, faster and faster. By the 1950s the world was losing one species of
plant and animal every month, by the 1980s one species *every week*. By the 1990s
it'll be one species every hour, and by the year 2000 the world will have lost $1\frac{1}{4}$
million species – that's a quarter of the living diversity of this earth.

Why are we losing them? In some cases, people are actually going out killing
and collecting them for personal pride or profit. However, the main explanation

for their loss is that we are destroying and polluting their very habitats. As you read this book, every minute sees the destruction of at least 50 hectares of natural and semi-natural vegetation. Some is cleared to produce food, some for building or construction work, but the vast amount is simply the result of unplanned exploitation for short-term gain by governments, companies, and individuals, many of whom should know better.

But why does it matter if the world loses a few strange plants and animals? It matters because extinction is forever. With those plants and animals, however strange and exotic, goes a slice of the world's genetic resource, a resource which took at least 3.6 billion years to develop, a resource which keeps the world alive and habitable. It's got to stop, not just because we don't want our grandchildren to grow up in a world without gorillas, whales, tigers and elephants, but because those genetic resources are of vital importance to all our futures.

The diverse populations of some five million different sorts of plants and animals maintain the fertility of the soils; cleanse rivers, lakes and seas; maintain levels of oxygen and carbon dioxide in living balance in the atmosphere; water the dry earth with sweet rain which is neither too acid or too caustic; and maintain the genetic diversity of life. This diversity means that environmental catastrophe and change won't lead to the total destruction of all our life-support systems; it allows the complete system of life to adapt, to make rapid use of any new situation, to overcome the problems thrown in its way. Impair that diversity any more, and we do it at the planet's peril, and that's our peril too because it's the only planet we've

Why this relentless bulldozing of species-rich rainforest? There may be a cure for cancer in there …

got. The analogy has been used of a space shuttle losing one by one the ceramic tiles which make re-entry a cool probability. But it is of course much worse than that, because our Space Shuttle Earth includes the whole works, space station, probe, mission control and all. What is more, just as mission control is starting to make new breakthroughs, producing better chances of survival through genetic and biological engineering, we are systematically destroying the very tools and raw materials on which it all depends, the raw materials of future success and survival.

We can clean up the mess, we can even stick the tiles back into place. We can turn the tide of destruction. But we cannot replace lost species and without them we are impotent in the face of mounting disaster. There is no other stock of resources which offers us the same potential. Their rapid loss is our planet's greatest degradation. We are in effect stealing our children's future. In the words of the American naturalist, William Beebe –

'The beauty and genius of a work of art may be reconceived, though its first material expression be destroyed: a vanished harmony may yet again inspire the composer; but when the last individual of a race of living things breathes no more, another heaven and earth must pass away before such a one can be again.'[11]

If the most important resource of all is genetic diversity, nowhere are genes more diverse than in the tropical rain forest. The world's rain forests contain about four-fifths of the living mass of all land vegetation, and yet only cover 8% of the world's land area. They are the most diverse on earth, the culmination of the whole process of evolution. They also are home to over two-fifths of the earth's plant and animal species. The forests of South East Asia contain at least 25,000 species of flowering plants, and the Malay Peninsula itself 7900 plants. A single hectare of forest in Manaus contains over 235 different species. The Sunda shelf area of South East Asia is home to 297 different mammals and over 732 species of birds, almost twice as many as the total species stock of birds and mammals found in the whole of Western Europe – an area four times the size. The tropical and sub-tropical forests are a vast gene bank from which many of our important food plants have originated: rice, millet, cassava, yam, banana, pineapple and sugar cane; and they still contain diverse, evolving populations of their wild relatives. The forests are a vital resource which is increasingly essential for the continuous process of plant breeding which improves the disease resistance and yield of the wild plants' high-tech brothers and sisters.

They are also the earth's main warehouse of industrial plants, our primary sources of raw materials like latex resins, dyes, essential oils, camphor, carnuba and a whole pharmacopoeia overflowing with everything from oral contraceptives to biological insecticides. The great forests are a veritable Aladdin's cave, with most of the jewels still waiting for straight-forward selection and upbreeding, not to mention a bit of polished high-tech engineering. What is more, less than only 1% of the species have even been screened for their potential use. And as many as 50% haven't even been accorded the complicated privilege of a Latin name in the record books. Take your pick from a few of those we do know, like the rosy periwinkle. This beautiful little pink-and-white flower of the forest edge, a close relation of our hardy evergreen periwinkle, is a real life-saver. It contains two alkaloids called vinblastine and vincristine which have provided a basis for the successful treatment of Hodgkin's disease and are being successfully deployed in the treatment of childhood leukaemia. Not to be outdone, its temperate cousin produces vincamine, now under investigation in France as an agent to delay senility. The seeds of the glory lily are a rich source of an alkaloid which alleviates gout. The African-based yojimbe tree, a member of the coffee family, appears to produce a really rejuvenating aphrodisiac. Then there is tubocurarine which comes from a tropical liana and makes open-heart surgery a practical, everyday happening. The list is long and growing thanks to the fact that Western medicine has at last begun to look beyond its own sphere of complacency. So new products from the disappearing rain forests are creating health, wealth and work for people across the globe.

With all this potential waiting to be realized, we really do have the where-withal to solve some of the world's many problems. Yet as we write, the Great Green Forest is losing its gleam. Its treasures are heading for the refuge of the *Red Data Book* (of threatened species). Every year, approximately 50 million acres of tropical forests are being destroyed. They are burned to provide prairies for cattle barons to feed the hamburger stalls of Europe and the United States. They are flooded by huge dam developments to create electricity for which there is no local need. They are felled by timber companies to make furniture, chip-board, and paper pulp for western use. These activities make jobs and money for a few people for a short time, but in the end they are all doomed: the soil is too fragile and the rain too heavy to sustain extensive grazing and cultivation; there is no re-planting to replace fallen trees; no reseeding to provide protection for the soil. There are also human casualties: the people of the forest, Indian tribes like the Amazonian Yanomami and Bara, African tribes like the Baka and Mubuti Pygmies, are driven from their homes. As their contact with the forest is severed, so also disappears their knowledge of its genetic resources, the 'librarianship' of its plants and medicines.

The Indians led ecologically-sustainable lives in the forest, only taking out what they knew could reproduce or what they could put back in. They were the eyes and ears of the forest, its ethno-scientists and genetic engineers, who experimented with nature and used it to supply their every need. To them and their knowledge of leaf, tree, branch, root, animal and insect, we owe the discovery of the basic ingredients of a wide range of modern medicines. We, the journeymen of the great voyages of discovery, in our arrogance have only scratched the surface.

The Indians were in no doubt that if you destroyed the rain forest, disaster followed. In a legend of the Kuma Indians of Panama it was said that tall trees supported the sky. If you cut them down, everything would fall apart. In another forest legend, this time from the Gaghuju Aborigines of Northern Australia it is said that if anyone sets fire to the trees they will be struck blind by the spirits of the forest blowing the smoke back into their faces . . . Through gene loss, through the destruction of natural diversity with its in-built buffering power, the smoke is blowing back in our faces. Carbon once stored in trunks and branches is released as carbon dioxide into the atmosphere on such a massive scale that it threatens natural balance. The replacement of a massive canopy of trees, all drawing water up into the atmosphere, by semi-deserts, not only alters river flow but changes the humidity. This has a knock-on effect on all our climates, local, national and international. The seeds of disaster are being sown in the air as well as on the ground.

Their world crashing down with the trees around them, the Indian tribes themselves are disappearing. They are yet another genetic loss, the destruction of human diversity by greed and 'progress'. Many of the aboriginal tribes in South America and India are heading for extinction. Their forest home gone, many headed for the shanty towns on the edges of new cities for an altogether unhealthier type of subsistence living – from the leavings of the urban wilderness. Their previously rewarding ways of life just disappeared and many of them died. Other tribes have almost been completely wiped out, like the Brazilian Kreen-Akore. And the existence of at least thirty-four other tribal groups in Brazil, over 6700 former guardians of the rain forest, is threatened by one development in the north west of the country – the huge Polonoroeste Dam project.

The world isn't just losing its tropical rain forests. This mass genetocide is taking place across the globe. New agricultural technology which once appeared to offer nothing but hope is in part to blame. Super cereals, vegetables and fruits, all bursting with productive potential, promised to feed the growing world and make all the farmers rich. It did much in that direction, but at the same time it changed the face of many landscapes, turning them from a productive patchwork of people and nature, living in relative rustic harmony, into prairie meccas of agro-farming. In some places the profits looked so good, especially where these were backed by government subsidies, that the caring inheritance of farming families was replaced by farm managers working for quick-profit investment companies. All this has resulted in the massive destruction of natural and semi-natural habitats. Woodlands and hedgerows, have been grubbed up. Wetlands, moorlands, and uplands have been drained and re-fertilized, pesticides and fertilizers have been sprayed in ever-increasing circles. In some parts of Britain, increased visitor pressure and even over-zealous plant-collecting have added to the problems. The net result has been to make the commonplace rare, to divide what were continuous populations into distinct units out of context with each other and so divorced from genetic continuity and interchange, to make some of our own native varieties extinct. All this is part of world-wide genetic erosion.

In Britain no less than nineteen species of native plant have melted with the snows of recent time. Gone are the summer ladies' tresses orchid, marsh fleawort, broad-leaved centaury and the curiously-named hairy spurge and interrupted brome. None were unique to the UK, they grow elsewhere, but these were the stalwarts whose genetic traits allowed them to thrive in the soils and climates of our land, part of our genetic heritage. No less than seventy-nine species of bird,

Autumn lady's tresses – this orchid's close yet genetically distinct relative, the Summer lady's tresses, is now extinct.

thirty-nine types of wild animal and sixty-two species of plant have found refuge only in the comforting arms of the law. These include once commonplace species like the woodlark, the kingfisher and the barn owl, and shy beauties like the lady's slipper orchid, the adder's tongue spleenwort and the spring snowflake. Britain's seasons will never be quite the same again.

For many of these disappearing plants the word *officinale* signified that their virtues earned them a place not only in *Culpepper's Herbal* but also in the pharmacopoeia of Britain. Some even still deserve a historic and honourable place in medical history. Digitalin from the foxglove is still used in the treatment of heart problems, and extract of willow provided the blueprint for aspirin. Likewise in our hedgerows and fields can be found wild thyme, carrots and cabbages, and at least 130 other food plants, all with wild tastes and wild genes, which could be put to use in the future. These are all home-grown genes for our home-grown greens.

The fact is that the western palate doesn't pay too much attention to home-based things. It is heavily dependent upon imported foodstuffs from across the globe, the genetic pickings of many lands. This isn't true just of exotic fruits and spices, but of our daily staples, many of which have an international origin, like the wheat in our bread, pasta and flour. Its ancestors were, and still are, found growing in the fertile crescent of the Middle East; and even in Ethiopia, now drought-dry, gene- and grain-stricken.

Opposite
English hay-meadow – an irreplaceable genetic inheritance – yet over 95% have disappeared since the 1950s.

Rice, now grown all over the warmer world, came first from South East Asia. Corn on the cob, which puts the crackle in our cornflakes and produces the corn starch and oil which goes into many of our processed foods, originated in Central America. Corn today is a principal food plant of the Western World. More than 300 million tonnes are produced every year and processed into flour, oil, animal feed, cereals, bourbon and popcorn. It's a perfect product of genetic engineering across the ages. The butter-drenched cylinder of golden ears sitting on our plate is a hybrid monster, bearing very little relationship to its wild ancestor Teosinte, the Mexican 'Mother of Maize'.

But to keep these hybrid varieties healthy and productive, we have to keep dipping back into the gene pool of their native countries. We need to keep extracting genes from wild species to ensure that high yields are maintained. In order to do this we are at it again, stealing the world's most precious resource – genetic diversity. Whether we like it or not, we've all been receiving stolen goods from the broken banks of the world's gene stocks. We've all become accomplices in the world's worst international crime – the Great Gene Robbery.

SPUD'S LAW

One of the world's most popular foods, the humble potato, was a victim of genetic theft. To rediscover its origins, we have to head for the High Andes of Peru and Ecuador in South America.

The modern British potato doesn't bear much relationship to its Peruvian ancestors, and as for the crisp ... In Britain alone, tens of millions of packets of crisps are eaten every day, and that's over 600,000 tonnes of real potatoes every year. The trouble is that virtually every one of these crisps, over 20 billion individual potato slices, has been processed from just one single variety. Each crisp is a clone, containing *identical* genes. The variety used has been bred especially for conversion into crisps.

They're high-yielding – up to 20 tonnes per hectare – and uniform in shape and size. Worst of all, they are totally bland and uniform in taste, so that they won't interfere with all the artificial flavourings that the manufacturers expect both them and us to soak up.

It's a reflection of the general trend that more and more of our crops are becoming over-dependent on a very narrow genetic base. In Britain, half the potatoes produced are made up of just five varieties. In the United States it's even worse – three quarters of the spuds consumed cover only four varieties.

Each crisp potato lined up on the factory conveyor belt is one of a huge crop of multi-million potato clones all the same size and weight, and with the same susceptibility to disease. So if one plant in the field falls to fungal disease, the rest will follow. That's what happened in the Irish Potato Famine of 1846, when a million people died of starvation. Back in those days, potatoes were not nearly so uniform or highly-bred as they are today, but the lack of species diversity meant that no potato was resistant to the predations of a virulent strain of *Phytophthora infestans* – potato blight – a fungus which produced black spots, a white mould on the leaves, and turned the tubers into a white, poisonous pulp. The potatoes, and a million poor people, were prematurely driven into the dust. Now, just like Ireland in the 1880s, plant uniformity dominates the condition and demands of the market place. The money from the clone crisp operation feeds a huge, but fragile farming enterprise propped up with bank overdrafts, subsidies and imported fertilizers. The only thing which keeps the whole system from collapsing is the plant breeders' ability, so far, to keep just one jump ahead of new strains of disease.

At a Plant Breeding Station in Pentlandfield, Scotland, they've been keeping one jump ahead of potato blight for fifty years. In their crisp, constant-temperature spud room you'll find a refreshing treasure house of potato varieties of all shapes and sizes.

Inside each plant is a storehouse of genetic information, which gives it a distinctive appearance, allows it to have productive tubers which boil well, stand up to drought, wind, disease and a complete range of pests. They're all varied enough to earn individual names, like 'Craig's Defiance', or the more moderate 'Craig's Alliance' and 'Pentland Envoy', and represent just a minute fraction of the enormous genetic diversity of the potato as originally found in its native home on the foothills of the Andes. The heath and heather of Scotland may be a far cry from the land of the llama and the condor, but it's a connection that needs to be sustained to maintain the essential diversity to keep some potatoes disease-free for the future.

The Spanish brought the potato to Europe in the 16th century as a souvenir

The search for Eldorado – De Soto in Peru – and the beginning of the end for another tribal civilization.

Left *Potato crop western-style –
a monotonous and vulnerable
mono-crop.*

Below *Peruvian potato crop –
rich and diverse in colour,
shape, flavour and disease
resistance.*

from one of their many trips to the natural paradise of South America. These 'brave' Conquistadores destroyed tribal culture after culture in their greed for an 'Eldorado' which they never found. And they never realized the true value of the humble potato. When the early Spanish adventurers finally tired of their South American holiday they left it in pretty poor shape: an apalling legacy of exploitative social structures, warring factions and a division between wealth and poverty unparalleled across the globe. That legacy remains and is behind much of the destruction of the great South American wilderness areas, particularly Amazonia.

But at least they left the wild potato. In Peru alone there are over 150 different, known species to choose from, breed from and to produce new seed stock. They're even watched over by a potato deity, a divine upholder of 'spud's law' – the Nazca, Potato God. From these, the Incas, Aztecs, Quechuas and their successors, the traditional Peruvian smallholders, have managed over the last thousand years to cultivate over *3000* different varieties. Each single product of this miracle of domestic genetic engineering has developed a different shape, colour, texture and taste. Eaten today, there is no need to add flavour to this wholesome, nutritious food. The Peruvian farmers grow a dozen or more varieties in one plot. If a disease comes it only affects part of the crop. So most of the plants survive. Some of them grow well in the hotter lowlands, some in the forest areas and some up near the snow-line. All are genetic offshoots of the original wild potato, an alpine plant that likes a refined upland atmopshere, a cut above all other vegetables. To keep these varieties healthy, there is still a need for its wild ancestors, and a need for these ancestors to stay wild, in a primeval state of ever-recharging genetic purity. The gene-rich diversity of the pristine wild spud is essential to keep the potato world going round and growing sound. The international potato people know it too, and every year they send teams of scientific explorers up into the Andean Mountains in search of the wild plants, the alpha and omega of the potato set.

These latter-day Conquistadores take the genes as their prizes back to breeding stations in their own countries and use them to breed bigger and 'better' spuds, many of which need lots of fertilizer and pesticides. The international chemical companies have a big hand in plant-breeding, for whether or not it's done with profit afore-thought there's a lot of money to be made from a successful variety, particularly if your fertilizer is being used to grow it. All in all, it's just a continuation of the old South American rip-off: plant-gene pooling is in effect plunder under another name. And the Great Gene Robbery isn't just confined to potatoes. The same is shamefully true for all the great staple foods – wheat, maize, rice and beans. The gene banks of the Third World are keeping the First World overfed. The excuse is they may have the genes, but we have the techniques and the money to develop their vast potential. What is more we have the marketing power and we need the control to make it all profitable.

However, the rip-off is biting back, and the plant breeders and even the environmental scientists are getting worried. The gene pool into which they have been dipping so freely and frequently over the years is beginning to dry up. In the case of the poor old spud, the rough tough wilderness land where it has grown undisturbed for millions of years, is under increasing pressure from change, destruction and development. It is being ploughed up for farming, concreted for roads and invaded by all sorts of weeds and grazing aliens and by uncontrollable pests and diseases. The wild spuds are being driven slowly down the road to extinction. What's more, all those primitive varieties which the locals grow are also threatened. Most of these are poor yielders, and the agents of the new breed spuds are now tempting the peasant farmers with higher-yielding varieties. Imagine the sales line: 'Grow more to the acre, grow nice, well-shaped, productive plants, grow your own and you will have so many surplus to your needs that you will make a fortune.' At the market place, new spuds for old is the tempting cry. So those primitive cultivated varieties are beginning to disappear too. And again, the same thing's happening with all the other major food crops worldwide. Farming developments and the destruction of wilderness are threatening almost every genetic resource we have. The intentions are often good, more farm-land, higher yields, less starvation, jobs in processing etc., but the outcome for genetic sustainability is catastrophic. In one infamous bad example the workers on an aid project in Afghanistan encouraged farmers to eat their old seed and to plant new high-yielding varieties in their place. The old primitive varieties, effectively the genetic heritage of a millennium, disappeared in a few mouthfuls of porridge.

The First World influence has been awesome. Those new super cereals and other crops were too tempting, especially when handed out with all the gleam and glint of tractors and modern farming. When a few crops later, the escalating costs of fuel, fertilizers, pesticides and herbicides could not be met, it was already too late. The diversity of seed stock which had sustained them and their forefathers with nothing more sophisticated and expensive than muck and luck was gone, swept into extinction under the not-so-magic carpet of progress. In order to counteract this self-serviced catastrophe, the plant breeders have set up enormous gene banks. One such establishment is the International Potato Centre located outside Lima on the coastal plain of Peru. Here the precious potato germ-plasm is stored; new potatoes are being developed by crossing wild and tame varieties, and true potato seed is being researched and developed to replace the much bulkier potato tuber. Another branch of this potato bank is located at Huancayo higher up in the Andes where every year thousands of different varieties are planted out to maintain a 'living' gene bank.

The money for gene or seed banks comes largely from western countries through the auspices of the World Bank. They retain tight controls over their blue-chip investments – some £25 million worth every year across the globe. Some gene banks are heavily guarded with fences and machine guns, and access is strictly controlled, and unlike your average street bank, the manager is not always so kindly disposed to grant a loan, even to the original owners. Woe betide any Third World plant breeders who want to make a return on their original investment. There are tight controls on trade, because it's big business, and the banks are keen to prevent rival interests or powers from stealing their strains. Our genetic inheritance is an international asset, which should be freely available to all who require it, yet it has been privatized. Genes mean profit. The argument is that gene banking is a precarious business. Not only are there the institutional-ized and the unofficial robbers to worry about; but there are political insecurities, the predations of changing governments, unstable political regimes and the threat of destruction by war and civil strife.

Most ludicrous of all, a power cut, a faulty contact or a simple throw of the wrong switch in the high-tech growing conditions of the gene bank and the 'conserved' genetic resources of a continent's entire wilderness can be extin-guished in a matter of minutes. It's a modern tragedy in four parts: Act One is decimation of the virgin wilderness area, Act Two is the robbery, in Act Three the spoils are deposited in the bank and in Act Four there is a genetic holocaust which takes place as the lights go down. Even without a catastrophe they are doomed, for however well-protected the bank, the genetic information impris-oned in those fruit seeds are shut off from the processes of nature, the hurly-burly of environment which gave them their diverse genetic strengths. Shut away these must, in time wane and wither. With no hope of replenishment from the wild their chances of survival become even less.

The Gene Banks can only lock away a minute segment of the world's genetic diversity. When the investors, the plant breeders, developers, agro- and petro-

The ultimate scheme to preserve the species – but who's managing the Ark now?

chemical companies withdraw from their current account, they place just one or two known hybrids on the market. These are hybrids which they hope everybody will want to use that year. So it is that the whole world moves from genetic diversity and adaptibility to the uniform problem of monoculture.

To ram the point home, put on your coat and go outside for a quick look in your own back yard. Just think of the changes that have taken place in the average family garden over the last forty years. At one time it was just a little bit of culture, of human planning and intervention and an awful lot of nature. Recollect how the flower garden used to look in Flora Thompson's day, when she wrote *Lark Rise to Candleford*:

> 'Narrow paths between high, built-up banks supporting flower borders, crowded with jonquils, auriculas, forget-me-nots and other spring flowers, led from one part of the garden to another. One winding path led to the earth closet in its bower of nut-trees half-way down the garden, another to the vegetable garden and on to the rough grass plot before the beehives. Between each section were thick groves of bushes with ferns and capers and Solomon's seal, so closed in that the long, rough grass there was always damp. Wasted ground, a good gardener might have said, but delighted in its cool, green shadiness.
>
>   Nearer the house was a portion given up entirely to flowers, not growing in beds or borders, but crammed together in an irregular square, where they bloomed in half-wild profusion. There were rose bushes there and lavender and rosemary and a bush apple-tree which bore little red and yellow streaked apples in later summer, and Michaelmas daisies and red-hot pokers and old-fashioned pompom dahlias in autumn and peonies and pinks already budding.'

Part of the garden was the vegetable plot or allotment. Here the old men of the villages would gather in the rosy summer evenings or spring moonlight nights to tend their harvests of currant and gooseberry bushes, celery, marrows, and the potatoes of all the old varieties— Ashleaf, Kidney, Early Rose, Magnum Bonum, and the huge mis-shapen but prized White Elephant. For genetic diversity it was wonderful, nature and culture working hand in hand.

Sadly now it's largely all gone. In comparison, how does your garden grow? With hybrid bells, plastic shells and euro-gnomes all in a row? White elephant potatoes may be a thing of the past, but they've been replaced by new mons-trosities, like the directives of the EEC that control the numbers and types of seed varieties available in our market gardens. The EEC's white elephant is its Common Agricultural Policy which restricts us to two or three seed varieties. Gone is the huge choice of vegetable seeds with which we could once fill our vegetable plots, and later on our tables and tummies. Gone also are granny's wild garden hollyhocks and wallflowers, foxgloves and larkspurs. Gone are the old russet apples which used to grow above them, the trees showering them with pink and white petals every spring. The old varieties have gone, just like the dodo, to the wall of extinction, and been replaced by the uniform, by the limited choice, soaking up artificial fertilizers, flood flavourings and additives. A dream of diversity lying shattered on a wasteground of uniformity. Even our own gardens participate in the Great Gene Robbery, the scandalous whittling away of the genetic diversity of our planet.

BANKING ON THE FUTURE

The Gene Banks are locking up the secrets, seeds and fruits of the past. But there are a few individuals and institutions around who are turning against the tide of gene bank complacency. They are investing in the fruits of the future, by fighting to preserve the few great natural gene banks we still have left. The custodian of some of the UK's prize plots of genetic diversity which are of priceless value to the heritage landscapes, gardeners and farmers of the future is the Nature Conservancy Council (NCC). This is a government body which protects against great outside pressure a national network of nature reserves and Sites of Special Scientific Interest (SSSI's). In these reserves wild nature is protected from human interference and allowed to evolve and diversify within at least semi-natural surroundings.

Come with us on a ramble to two of the NCC's prize genetic capital assets: the first located in the heart of the old English down grasslands of Wiltshire; the second in the High Pennines.

In the midst of a vast ocean of mono-tone Wiltshire farm desert lies a 700-acre oasis of natural pasture: Parsonage Down Farm. This was passed on to the NCC and the nation by its former owner the late Robert Wales. He was an enlightened man worried by the trend towards mono-tone agriculture and the greed that went with it, and was determined to pass on to further generations a farmed paradise of genetic diversity which he had himself inherited from others. The downland as a result is a naturalists' haven, particularly between spring and autumn when the chalk grassland is ablaze with flowers, mostly yellow in the spring, white in high summer, blue and deep blue in late summer and moving to purple in the autumn. Before high-yield corn became king less than twenty years ago the whole grassland area around Parsonage Down was just the same – a massive meadow of rainbow colours changing through the seasons.

But Parsonage Down isn't just a paradise for wildlife. It's a working low-input, low-output profitable farm, providing most of its own resources; feed for hardy cattle and fodder for sheep; the animals graze together, more-or-less as nature had intended. The farm manager is Bill Elliot, whose father and grandfather before him had also worked Parsonage Down. He practises careful husbandry, avoiding overstocking of animals, observing a series of seasonally-adjusted grazing rotations, and preserving the natural features of the land, its humps, hollows and anthills, and thus conserving the plentiful wildlife it attracts. As a result, there are as many as forty-two different plant species to the square metre, from herbs like eyebright to salad burnet, orchids and quaking grass, a whole host of flowering meadow plants. Added to these is a whole range of insects,

*Kew Gardens – the Victorian's
botanic version of the Ark*

molluscs and other tiny organisms – some of them still new to the record books. It's a veritable storehouse of genetic diversity: two plant-pots full of samples keeps a university laboratory full of botanists and geneticists busy for an entire year. Each sample is as natural as the farm day is long. There's not a drop of 'added value' in sight: the soil on which some of the specimens are grown has never even been ploughed. Some of that downland is part of an ancient Saxon field system, just one step away from virgin whole earth. The land is not only gene-rich, it is a garner of mineral riches, of magnesium and calcium which maintain a healthy nutritional balance in soil, plant, insect, animal and ultimately man too. Even the downland butter is locally renowned for its rich and earthy taste.

The fact that what is in effect a nature reserve like Parsonage Down can be run as a profitable farm enterprise is proof that the preservation of genetic diversity can be achieved without extra subsidy and without taking land out of production. Parsonage Down is a natural gene bank, a solid inexpensive investment in the natural wealth of the past for the benefit of present and future generations. There are many more such natural gene banks in the UK, run as SSSI's or Nature Reserves by the NCC or as Local Nature Reserves by County Conservation Trusts. The total amounts to over 2000 sites spread over 550,000 acres of land. This is a drop in the ocean compared to the total land area taken up by intensive farming, urban or industrial development. But it's a critical drop in the natural ponds of a worldwide gene pool which is shrinking daily. These little ponds in the big pool are not just static natural prisons, vaults frozen in space and time-dependent on artificial atmospheres and high-energy growth stimulation, but living, breathing ecosystems. Some of them are also working agricultural systems, like the ancient woodland genetic reserves of Monk Wood and Staward Pele Wood SSSI's in the High Pennines, home to ancient sessile oaks, rich lichens and sub-alpine flora.

These sites also provide a permanent timber resource for local estate workers, and a valuable, attractive amenity for locals and visitors alike.

Even the less hospitable Widdybank Fell on the damp remote High Pennine top of Upper Teesdale is a working farm grazed by cattle and sheep. The area is a paradise for walkers and amateur botanists, making extensive use of the Pennine Way and local nature trails. Its sugar limestone rock and soils support unique colonies of rare alpine flowers, herbs and grasses which have thrived there since the retreat of the great glaciers of the last Ice Age, some 12,000 years ago. No artificial gene bank could possibly recreate or reproduce the geological, botanical and climatic conditions which have brought together the gentle evolution of the rare plants of Upper Teesdale, from the shrubby cinquefoil and hoary rockrose, the bog sandwort and yellow mountain saxifrage to the glories of the spring gentian and birds'-eye primrose.

At least some of the genetic inheritance of Great Britain is safe in the hands of official and voluntary bodies. What of the rest of the world and especially the great tropical forests, Nature's supreme genetic reservoirs? These support most of the world's flowering plants — some 155,000, out of an estimated total of 250,000. Each plant species supports in turn at least thirty other dependent organisms, only a tiny percentage of which have been systematically studied. What is being done to conserve that wealth of endangered genetic diversity?

Where else can we go in the world where genuine gene-preserving action is taking place? Thankfully there are a few such places, and the number is growing.

At an international level the World Conservation Strategy team put together in 1980 a global programme for the protection of the world's richest genetic resource areas. Tropical rainforests, as ecosystems of exceptional diversity, where potentially useful yet threatened varieties and species are concentrated, were earmarked as a major priority for action. According to the WCS team, the rainforest genetic reservoir, as a global heritage potentially beneficial to all mankind, requires not just national but also international sponsorship and protection. Since the forests occur mostly in the developing countries of South America, Africa and South Asia, they suggest that funds for their protection should be raised from the developed countries and commercial organizations to compensate for access to their rich genetic reserves. The rainforests would thus be treated just like real banks. Customers, like seed companies and industries, would pay for the privilege of using them. If they wanted to withdraw samples of wild species for genetic engineering, hybrid crop production, pest control, medical or industrial use, they would have to deposit the necessary cash, advice and help to keep the bank operating for future use. Such a measure would force the international market to appreciate the true economic value of the rainforests; it would also involve them in a positive process of responsible, sustainable exploitation.

Other more localized suggestions by the WCS team for action include the establishment of new fuelwood and industrial plantations to offset the depletion

of existing rainforest resources. Yet another idea would be to create buffer zones for concentrated rural development on good soil at the edges of the rainforests, so that local people would be offered alternatives to the current trend of clearing the forests for short-stay agricultural abuse. The WCS team also argue that there should be a programme of re-afforestation to replace the forests that have already been uprooted. The administration and protective powers of those responsible for managing the forests also need strengthening, if these initiatives are to be sustained.

Species-rich Himalayan flower meadow beneath Nanda Devi – mountain of Gaia, the earth goddess.

Already there are some good examples of these principles in action. In Indonesia, with the help of the World Wildlife Fund and the IUCN, co-sponsors of the WCS strategy, the national government has produced a Master Plan for the conservation and sustainable utilization of Irian Jaya, the Indonesian half of New Guinea. This vast virgin wilderness is sub-divided by the Plan into a series of reserves which are graded into classified sections ranging from high levels of exploitation to totally undisturbed conservation areas. Conservation and resource-use measures appropriate to each section have been worked out and are being implemented. The WWF have initiated a similar scheme in Madagascar. Seven new ecosystem reserves have been earmarked and an educational programme has been set up to encourage local people to become involved in conserving their forests while making use of them as a 'cultivated' crop.

In recent years as a result of the tropical forest campaigns of the WWF and a

'Chipko' women from the Garhwal forests in the High Himalayas – they 'embraced' the trees in a desperate attempt to stop their felling.

whole range of other and some even more vociferous environmental bodies, there has been a veritable rainforest of similar schemes combining conservation with rural development and education, a real rustling in the tropical undergrowth. Most notable are the agri-forestry schemes in Kenya, Thailand and the Philippines which combine tropical silviculture with fruit and vegetable production. The latter are cultivated between the trees of existing plantations. The high trees trap humidity and draw up deep water; they shelter man, beast and the lower canopy of fruit trees, bushes and vegetable rows and they provide fuel and raw materials. It's a complete, recycling, green and healthy ecosystem: man sustains the trees with planting, manure and careful husbandry of their wild genetic resources. The trees in turn hold the soil and offer sustenance to man.

The organization Earthlife has initiated a campaign to secure international investment that will set up and sustain the Korup rainforest in the Cameroons as an international wildlife park, the property of 60,000 individual share-holders from across the globe, to be put in trust for the benefit of future global generations. Earthlife hopes this will be a demonstration project which will lead the way to many others. Support by individuals, like the shareholders of Korup, is critical to the success of this and many other schemes. At the end of the day, it is the actions and sense of responsibility of individuals within such international organizations which will bring about political change and turn the tide of rainforest destruction.

Most important of all, however, are the home-based grass-roots movements, for even if they are spawned from despair, they are working from within. A magnificent model for local action has been provided in the temperate forests of Garhwal in the High Himalayas, home of some of the most disastrous deforestation, subsequent soil erosion and genetic destruction on the face of the global garden. The Garhwal hills are also home to the first women of the Chipko movement, who have 'embraced' their trees in a desperate attempt to stop the destruction. The Chipko movement has its inspiration in an Old Indian legend. According to this, many centuries ago, when the hills were green with trees, the local Maharaja, or 'Great King' started clearing the hill sides for timber. Local village women, one for each day of the year, determined to protect the trees which provided them with fuel and subsistence, entered the forest and wrapped their arms around the trees. They refused to move and were hacked to pieces along with the trees by the king's men. On hearing of their bloody sacrifice, the Maharaja vowed to protect the forest and never again violate the beliefs of these proud local people.

Many years later, in the 1970s the successors to the Maharaja's forest inheritance included the Government forestry department and groups of commercial loggers. Over the years, these bodies had become involved in a massive programme of deforestation to supply the paper and timber needs of India's resource-hungry urban areas. The traditional fuelwood supplies of the villagers were being depleted: the village women were having to walk up to 15 kilometres every day to collect firewood and treeleaf animal fodder. Soil erosion, landslides and floods were becoming commonplace. In 1970, the Alakhnanda River flooded, hundreds of homes were destroyed, 200 people died and 100 miles of irrigation canal became clogged with silt. By 1973, seeing the chaos mounting around them as a result of forest destruction, the women of Garhwal acted. The forest companies were stopped in their tracks as village women rallied to save the trees from the axe by emulating their legendary forebears and putting their arms around them. In 1974 the Chipko women, (the word 'Chipko' means 'to embrace') saved 2500 trees from being sold off for timber at the village of Reni by embracing them, singing 'This forest is our mother's home, we will protect it with all our might.'

News of this success spread and from that point on, similar protests started to take place all over India. Many forest areas were saved. By 1976, the passion and spirited devotion of the Chipko movement so impressed the Indian central government that they imposed a ban on all logging on hillsides above 1000 metres. Saved from the axe, the trees and soils of the High Himalayas could breathe again. The Chipko women did not rest. They sowed the seeds for a massive re-afforestation programme, integrating forestry care with local village life. More than 1 million cyprus, walnut, oak, poplar and other trees have been planted. Planting and environmental education camps have been set up, and local village discussion groups have led to a whole range of remedial sustainable and forestry projects. Many of these have attracted overseas funding, from the World Bank and other agencies, and now receive the strong support and encouragement of the central Indian government.

By their actions, these women had stemmed a tide of thoughtless destruction which threatened to undermine an entire mountain ecosystem, a genetic reserve of species and sub-species which would have been lost to future generations, and would have made the continuation of community as well as natural life eventually impossible. So too, the Green Belt movement in Kenya is again inspired and fired by women. Their aim is to plant a girdle of forest encircling every village, to slow soil erosion, provide green shade and eventually an on-the-doorstep supply of coppiced fuelwood.

Green, growing, sustainable hope is spreading round the world and though it may be too late for those 1.25 million species which are going to be erased from the face of the earth by the turn of this sad century, there is now a real chance for the rest. Clearly, if we are to preserve the gene banks and genetic diversity of the future from the predations of the present we will need all the international conventions, wildlife protection laws, rare-breed trusts, designated world centres of high genetic diversity, conservation master plans, nature reserves, wildlife parks, countryside acts, botanic gardens and even artificial gene banks we can get. But there will also have to be strict controls on the powers and activities of those multi-national vested interests which are encouraging the genetic erosion of our world, which profit from the destruction of the world's natural gene banks and in particular from the savage sacrilegious genetocide of its tropical rainforests.

In the turning of the genetic tide, action has to be simultaneously global and local. We can all play a positive part. We can boycott the fruits of destruction, the tropical hardwoods and the products of rare plants and animals. We can plant and preserve rare bits and pieces of our green inheritance. We can all afford to grow a little wilder and wiser every day. And we have to keep up the pace. Otherwise the international erosion of our genetic inheritance, the destruction of the diversity which floats across the world's species sea, could leave us with an arid beach, with no life on earth.

6 DAMNING THE FUTURE

BUILDING FOR PROFIT OR FOR PEOPLE?

You can't have even sustainable growth without development, but bad development eats away at the roots of sensible growth, leaving behind ecological and economic sickness, or a false, prematurely flowering growth that subsequently withers and dies. Big dams are the mega-monsters of bad development. These top-heavy environmental dinosaurs sum up all that is bad in our attitude to development, an attitude which gets in the way of real human progress.

We follow in the tracks of some of the more outlandish of these monsters, charting the destruction left behind in their wake. And we meet some of the dinosaur hunters who oppose these schemes and have scored some notable victories in the past. We explore some examples of good development; and see real people-power in action.

NO DAM' GOOD

There must be times when even the most open-minded reader finds protestors boring, because maybe, they protest too much. But then have you ever heard an anti-protestor in full flood, like the spectator watching the Franklin River Dam protests in Tasmania. This is what he had to say:

> 'Just look at them. Hairy, good-for-nothing layabouts. Floating protestors . . . They might look as if they're skint – not a penny between the lot of them – but I bet Daddy dropped them off from his power boat . . . I wonder what it is this time? If it's not nuclear power or Greenham Common it's anything which smacks of progress. Moaning about the odd bit of tree clearance or pollution while all the time gorging themselves on the fruits of material progress.'

In the event the Franklin Dam scheme was overturned. The remarkable Huon Pinewoods, the flora and fauna of the beautiful river gorges, escaped by a whisper. But the anti-protestor's opinions still stand too. All too often, these days, environmentalists are looked upon as the elite, effete few who haven't even got their feet anywhere near the real ground. They're seen as being more interested in saving a few rare birds than allowing honest decent people to get on with the work they're doing. But without them our world's very life-support systems – the only hope we've all got of ever really feeding, housing and clothing all the people of this planet – are threatened. The Franklin River's contribution to the global life-support system may have been saved, but elsewhere, the destruction caused by large-scale, inappropriate development goes on.

In the developing world, big dams are all the rage, as fashionable as Coca-Cola and military dictatorships. Never have so many really huge dams been built at one time. And year by year, like the egos of their architects and the wallets of their construction agencies, they're getting bigger and bigger. So big, in fact, that they're fit to burst and unleash upon their supposed beneficiaries a tidal wave of destruction, debt and disaster.

Let's look at the example of the Itaipu dam on the border of Brazil and Paraguay in South America. It's so colossal, there's enough concrete to pave an entire motorway stretching from Paris to the Persian Gulf.

A hydro-electric dam harnessing the power of water and putting money into the pockets of the dam-builders – but, at what cost to the environment and long-term benefit?

Similar developments in Egypt dwarf, in volume, by seventeen times, the biggest of the great pyramids. They also drowned the sacred tombs of some of ancient Egypt's Pharaoh-gods and an awful lot of animals unable to escape quickly enough from the rising waters. The dams themselves even challenged the ancient, awesome powers of the Sun Emperors: they were so big that they had the power to disrupt weather patterns world-wide. So, too, the Itaipu developers appear almost to believe they have the power of divine intervention. Take a look at this extract from their handbook, entitled *Sculpture for a New Era*:

'The dam for the world's largest hydro-electric facility is finished. On the horizons which bounded the lands of the old Guarani Indians, that monumental mass of concrete, which holds back one of the seven largest rivers on earth, rises up like a delirious dream: a group of gigantic cathedrals tear away toward the sky with force and elegance, as the response by human engineering to a tremendous challenge of nature. It is impossible to escape the sensation of pride and amazement.

'What is most fascinating about the history of the world's largest hydro-electric plant is perhaps exactly this aspect of achievement, of the response to a huge challenge, of man's final triumph in taming nature which provides him with his survival. And this deed will be entered in the annals at the end of this century. First as a technical achievement. Subsequently as the guarantee for continued development: Itaipu will assure a supply of energy to the most industrialized sector of Brazil and for all of Paraguay for many many years to come, in this and in the next century. And finally, there are the lessons which this work will leave for posterity to be considered.'[12]

The writer then stakes the claim of Itaipu to immortality. He sees the mutual effort of the Brazilians and Paraguayans as deserving 'a chapter all by itself in the history of the great conquests by mankind.'

If the rhetoric of the handbook is anything to go by, Itaipu sounds truly wonderful. The positive benefits are very real indeed: Itaipu is expected to produce electricity equivalent to the output of ten large nuclear power stations, over 1 million kilowatts-worth every year. Unlike nuclear power, there's no radiation hazard, no by-products for nuclear warheads, no nuclear wastes or radio-active leaks. Neither are there acid pollutants or oil spills. Hydro-power involves a renewable energy resource – water, which can be used again and again to generate yet more power. And the water collected behind the colossal dam also can be used to irrigate crops. The dam, with its colossal skyline, towering falls and large expanse of water will no doubt attract many visitors, fishermen and pleasure seekers – all with cash to spend in the new townships and industries which will spring up in the area, by cheap and plentiful water power. Even wilderness enthusiasts who come to the area for a view of the spectacular Iguacu Falls only 60 kilometres away, will find it difficult to resist the new spectacle of a tamed wilderness.

Power, food and leisure, all from a good clean renewable resource: just what the environmentalists ordered you might think. But it's not that simple. The bill of health from Itaipu and big dams in general is, in fact, not at all clean. There are many social and environmental disadvantages and often the benefits do not measure to close scrutiny, from either economic or environmental viewpoints. Most big dams these days tend to be sited in the world's few remaining preserves of true wilderness — many are scheduled for the shrinking tropical rainforest areas of South America, Africa and South East Asia. To make way for them, huge sections of forest must be felled. And when the dam is built, even more forest is flooded. Some plants and animals are rescued and placed in 'havens' or sold off to zoos in foreign parts. Many more are drowned. Those that escape from man and the rising waters have to compete elsewhere for habitats in a rapidly shrinking natural world. Although the water will attract some new wildlife and provide habitats for fish, the species diversity will be less than before. The original plants and animals, the monkeys and jaguars, disappear, never to return.

And these big dams displace people too, hundreds of thousands of them. To make way for Itaipu, 50,000 people were moved away from an area of over 120,000 hectares, in which they had previously made a decent, reasonable living. Many of them can now be found rooting for work on the edges of 'civilization' in towns like Santa Monica. In pre-dam days, these people were peasant farmers, producing food mainly for their own family's consumption. Subsistence cropping served them well. They knew the limits of their local environment and knew that to push to too far would invite disaster. Suddenly, they had no choice. Insufficient land forced them to look elsewhere for a cash income. Flooded out of their land, they flood to the squalor of urban shanty towns in search of work.

Then come all the other attendant problems of re-settlement — conflict with other groups, unemployment, disease, lack of expertise in dealing with the new environments, and exploitation by new 'masters'. To the culture-shock and bewilderment of Indians and small-farmers forced for the first time out of their homes is added the shock of experiencing poverty and starvation for the first time. In the passage from the forest and fields of plenty to the cities and slums of affluence these are the people who are always the losers. There's no mention of their loss in the long list of gains set out in the Itaipu handbook. The counter argument may point out that, at least there's a lake, the locals could start a fishing industry to feed themselves. Certainly, for a short while after the flood all the nutrients released from the rotting vegetation and drowned wildlife would supply all the food needed for a bumper catch. But — and here's the real catch — this flush of fish only lasts as long as the nutrients are being released. Some weeds, like water cabbage, fern and hyacinth, seize the opportunity of making life impossible both for fish and fishermen. As the lake system settles down, less and less fish are caught. In fact, if the Itaipu area had been left alone, the original wild game and plentiful fish in the river would have yielded much more useful protein. And the thousands of Guarani Indians would have been able to stay in their homelands. Shortage of food is one problem, another is disease. The number and intensity of water-borne diseases tends to radically increase in the tropics when new lakes and irrigation canals replace the old predator-rich swamps and natural river systems. Malaria, parasitic flatworm, elephantiasis and river blindness are just a few of the many nasties on the increase.

The pro-dam lobby might say 'At least plenty of water is now available for irrigating local crops and getting better yields for the people.' But in fact there's much less than the dam designers thought. The water losses from evaporation are colossal. Up goes the water, but all the silt carried down by the river remains behind, gradually filling up the reservoir. That's not all, because as the water evaporates, the salts get more and more concentrated. The more you irrigate, the saltier the soil becomes, and rubbing salt on your vegetables while they are still in the ground is a recipe, not for added taste, but for disaster. Meanwhile, as the nutrient-rich silt, brought down by the river, gets trapped behind the dam, farmers and small-holders old and new are forced to buy in plant foods in the form of expensive fertilizers. The small farmers in greatest need are those who can least afford costly irrigation or fertilizers. They simply go bust, sell up to richer neighbours and head for the unlikely chance of finding work in the cities.

'OK', says the developer, 'fishing and farming are out, but how about tourism? Haven't the dammers calculated on a massive tourism infill after the flood, all packing it in to see the *Sculpture For a New Era*. Aren't there jobs in all that?' The answer to that one's easy. Sure there will be jobs for some, and tourists. But they'd all be wealthy Brazilians and foreign tourists. And they'll be holidaying in a handful of luxury hotels, contributing little to the local economy and not doing much for the local people. Without much to do, the locals will be on holiday too, but for them it'll be a permanent one, without pay and without pleasure. No wonder there's a resentment of foreigners, and so much trouble and tension in these South American societies.

Every year thousands of acres of tropical rainforest are burned to make way for big development schemes or intensive farming ... to the detriment of the local economy and the world's climate.

Shah Abbas Dam, Iran.

Hydro-electric power is, however, the biggest incentive for the dam-builders, 'surely', goes the argument, 'all that power potential leads to industry, wealth and jobs.' But this power is extremely expensive, heavily dependent on large capital investment by the World Bank and the other agencies. The Itaipu dam, when finally complete, will cost $15 billion — that's well over $100 for every person living in Brazil. Output from its eighteen turbines is to be shared with Paraguay. But the power released from only one turbine is more than enough to meet Paraguay's needs. The dam project is positively bloated with an excess of power — most of it unusable and unsaleable.

As in all walks of life, too much 'power' can quickly backfire, with tragic consequences: imagine the consequences of the barrier that holds back one of the world's most violent rivers and the whole thing collapsing. A once-in-a-lifetime event could become death-time on a horrendous scale. It has happened before; and when such disasters strike the poorer, more vulnerable Third World, about fifty times as many people are killed than would be the case in the developed world. So what happens in the less vulnerable First World, where the technology for these great dams was first developed? Surely there's a greater success rate there, with dams producing safe, much-needed power, good returns on investment and assurance of a plentiful water supply for thirsty industries?

Let's take a look at Kielder Water, in England's Border Country, former haunt of the Border Reivers – companies of Scotsmen who, in the 16th century plundered the countryside, pillaged homes and robbed the locals. The Reivers are now gone, but another kind of alien presence dominates the landscape and the lives of the people, and, some would say, accounts for just as much pillage and plunder. This particular form of rapine is one of the biggest man-made lakes in Europe, set in the heart of one of the biggest coniferous forests.

To make Kielder lake and dam, $1\frac{1}{2}$ hectares of land were flooded. Two hamlets, several farms, a long, winding road, a lot of field-edge habitats, traditional stone-walled farming and village life, and even the graves of some Border Reivers disappeared beneath Kielder's murky waters. When the dam was officially opened in 1982 and the waters started to collect and rise, a great silence fell upon the place, wiping out overnight the noise of centuries.

The object of this mega-exercise in water technology, the dream of a water board, was to supply water to industry on Tees-side, some 130 kilometres away. To get the water there, a 34-kilometre-long tunnel was built burrowing 300 metres beneath the high Pennines and connecting the rivers Tyne and Tees. However, the great blue dream of the Water Board turned out to be a great white elephant. A parliamentary enquiry concluded that the industry which demanded the water in the first place was in decline, and the demand for Kielder Water was likely to peter out completely. As a result Kielder never really came of age. Now it's a great watery grave of ill-conceived industrial and environmental plans. More than 200 million litres of excess water capacity and a great 12 kilometre-long lake. It remains a drain on public funds, costing local ratepayers £169 million, a bill which won't be paid off until AD 2010. As a mausoleum for the best-laid plans of the planners, Kielder is undeniably impressive, beautiful and dramatic, a great, man-made scenic feature. But apart from a few tourists, some water-sport types and fishermen, who has really benefited? The engineers, contractors and developers, of course ... and the local mosquito population. Kielder Water and its surrounding damp, acidic conifer woods are perfect breeding grounds for larvae which produce the biggest and best biting bugs in the business. If you're a visitor to Kielder you're bound to encounter them.

Meanwhile, dollar-bitten mega-buccaneers keep building more and more dams every year across the globe, in India, Malaysia, Africa, Thailand, China, the Philippines. There are those, like the Kariba and the Upper Volta, which have substantially improved the lives of the local people – although not without some costs. But these are the exceptions and the developers seem to forge ahead regardless. They're working towards a targetted 360,000-megawatt capacity that will flood over 20 million hectares of productive, irrigated land. Just six of the projected dams will flood nearly 3 million hectares of land; that's land lost forever. Thousands of animals and plants will become extinct, a single dam can threaten 400 different species. In total, the construction of these mega-monstrosities has the potential to destroy the lives of a billion people.

If it's all so disastrous, why do governments give the go-ahead for more and more superdams? The pursuit of large-scale development projects is tied up with conventional notions and ambitions of unlimited growth. The projects get bigger and bigger because the impulse is towards greater and greater growth. Big projects attract a lot of investment and employ a lot of people, creating many opportunities to try out new technology and support a wide range of service industries. The trouble is that sooner or later the dam bursts. As the development projects get bigger, and growth projects wilder, trouble builds up and inevitable collapse is quick and devastating. Take the example of Tees-side, one of the biggest industrial conurbations in Britain, where the local chemical and steel-making industries were to be the major users of the additional water supplies from the new dams at Kielder and at Cow Green. In the mid 1980s the boom bubble has burst. The additional water is not required, neither are the new local industrial plants, nor are the workers.

Kielder Reservoir and Dam, UK – a developmental white elephant?

The big dams are the best example there is of unwieldy and inappropriate development. There are others. Let's visit the town of Hartlepool, in Tees-side, to see what happens after the development bubble bursts.

The town was famous for its heavy industries of iron and steel, engineering and shipbuilding, employing over 12,000 people. Britain's very first nuclear power stations were designed and built in the area, and more recently, in 1968, construction started on another, this time in Hartlepool itself, slap-bang in the middle of a struggling, declining coalfield. The last was intended to meet the expanding industries' demand for more power, with the by-products of creating many new jobs and diversifying the local economy. Now, in the 1980s, the former industrial parks of Hartlepool are derelict. Iron and steel mills are shuttered up. The great doors and roofs of vast warehouses clatter forlornly in the wind. The big engineering firms are bankrupt. A sea of dingy *For Sale* signs dominate the skyline and there is no work, no opportunities for the people of Hartlepool. Half of all industrial workers have lost their jobs. And of the 500 miners that used to live in the town, only *four* remain. As for the great high-tech hope of the Hartlepool nuclear power station, this cost over £500 million of public money, was over ten years behind schedule and, in comparison to the heavy industries which preceded it, employs few workers.

Unemployment climbed to unprecedented levels. Hartlepool has become a wasteland of opportunities lost, misplaced investment and destroyed lives. When the recession struck, it was the big projects, big industries, and big employers which suffered most, but their collapse had repercussions right across the whole spectrum of industry and enterprise in the town. The environmental effect of recession on Hartlepool is considerable. No-one wants to invest, or build up new businesses and new dreams, in a wasteland of derelict factories, of polluted waterways, broken roads and decaying housing stock.

Many of the jobs and some of the investment has gone to the rising industrialized nations of the Third World, to Korea, Taiwan and Brazil, able through cheap labour and the local availability of raw materials to produce steel and manufactured goods at knock-down prices. Hartlepool, like much of the old industrialized world, cannot compete. With growth gone, there is no new development. But it's no good blaming, as some do, the big industries and low wages of the Third World for the loss of First World jobs. After all, workers in those countries don't want to receive low wages any more than we do. They're caught up in the same race and no-one is going to win. Most of us, Third World and First World, are going to lose unless the pattern of over-inflated industrial development changes radically, unless we're prepared to take a different direction altogether which is both economically and environmentally sustainable. The first step is to tackle our obsession with large-scale development projects, which disrupt the environment at the expense of more localized smaller-scale alternatives.

THE DAMBUSTERS

There are two types of dambusters – destructive and constructive. The first lot are the break-up and budget boys of the big corporations, whose blinkered approach to development drives developing countries into bankruptcy.

The 'dam' and 'bust' brigades, with their short-term view of development do no-one any favours. The people themselves ultimately finance these projects through rates, taxes and labour. In developing countries like Brazil where many dams are being built, even the lucky few who work often contend with horrendous employment conditions and miserably low wages. Most of their real earnings flow to the local rich and to First World countries. Much of the money raised by production and taxes is directly exported to repay the interest on huge loans raised from international moneylenders. Those countries with the dubious privilege of having several big developments under their belts, like Brazil, have found that their economies are totally dependent upon the will and whim of western banks. To massive and unpayable overseas debts are added spiralling inflation rates between 100% and 400% per annum. Debts are constantly defaulted on, and schemes are often abandoned half-way.

These are the politics of bankruptcy, the economies of madness. No wonder so many of these countries lurch from one kind of instability to another, switching their alliances with western powers one year to the eastern block the next. The repercussions are many. Third World politicians whose dreams of glory were spurred on by big investments are toppled in bloody *coups*: armaments, always in plentiful supply from foreign governments, furnish revolution, counter revolution, dictatorship, civil strife, war and, as always, the death of many innocents.

A report to the European Ecological Action Group by Goldsmith and Hildyard of the Wadebridge Ecological Centre in 1984, on the social and environmental effects of large dams, pointed to a very high level of economic deceit and account-fudging. Case histories from dams in California, USA, to Karnataka, India, reveal an extraordinary catalogue of ... fabrication of estimates; over-estimating of job creation, recreational, irrigation and flood control benefits; unrealistically low discount rates; discounting the energy costs involved in construction; ignoring the cost of de-commissioning the dams; over-estimating their 'useful life'; failing to count flooded land as a cost; and taking little or no account of the short- and long-term environmental costs. The evidence against big dams is overwhelming, the conclusions are damning. The report's authors conclude:

'It thus seems that those who stand to gain politically and financially from the building of a large dam are willing to go to inordinate lengths to ensure that it will be built. Among other things, they are willing purposefully to mislead those who must be persuaded of the dam's desirability and viability before the go-ahead to build it will actually be given. This they do by grossly exaggerating the dam's likely benefits and severely underestimating costs – in particular the social and ecological costs which are often totally ignored. The power, prestige and financial resources of the politicians, bureaucrats and industrialists involved in dam projects greatly facilitates that deceit – as does credulity and apathy of the public'.[13]

Economic 'miracles' based on foundations as shaky and dubious as these can be nothing but castles built on sand. Sooner or later the tide of destruction, bankruptcy, social tension and environmental bite-back — everything from salination to silting and even earthquake — will wash them away. The reputations of their engineers and builders will become lost in the sands of time.

While the developers and their schemes continue to go for bust, we'll visit the dambusters proper who try to damn these projects before the sand starts to get in everyone's eyes.

Pride of place amongst them is the Tasmanian Wilderness Society — the very ones who won the Franklin Dam battle. In 1983, they were prepared to risk injury, arrest and imprisonment to alert the world to the consequences of proposals to dam the upper tributaries of the Franklin River. At stake was a large area of temperate rainforest, containing a whole range of unique species and potential genetic resources. Damned also was wildlife as fine and special as sassafras plants, dogwoods, and the Tasmanian tiger, and stretches of dramatic natural waterways, a unique, world-scale recreational and wildlife heritage . . . and the last free river in Tasmania. Author James McQueen summed up the attitude of the protestors:

> 'It is the epitome of all the last forests, all the submerged lakes, all the tamed rivers, all the extinguished species. It is threatened by the same mindless beast that has eaten our past, is eating our present, and threatens to eat our future: that civil beast of mean ambitious and broken promises and hedged bets and tawdry profits.'[14]

The dambusters, ranging from passionate ecologists and students to local residents and international scientists, formed a blockade between the developers and the undeveloped fragile wilderness. Mass arrests followed. The subsequent hue and cry brought two vital factors to the attention of the public and the national election. Not only was the development ecologically destructive and irreversible, but it was also uneconomic. There was never any possibility that the huge investment involved in constructing the dam and altering the flow of this great river could be recouped by the energy benefits which might flow from the scheme. Tasmania already had on-line thirty-nine dams and twenty-six hydro-electric stations — one station for every 4362 electors on the state registry! The government had no energy-conservation schemes of the type put forward in Sweden and the USA which were saving up to 20% of power consumed and wasted. Furthermore, the Franklin scheme was going to produce only 180 megawatts of electricity — at a cost of over $8 million per megawatt; that's almost eight times the cost of many other hydro-electric schemes. The only real jobs created by the development numbered around thirty. There was certainly little or no long-term work for the local people. The scheme simply turned out to be yet another case of development for its own sake, of benefit only to the developers themselves, not to the people who, at the end of the day, had to pay for it. It was finally damned by the faulty economic logic of its promoters; public opinion and political pressure saved the day and the scheme was abandoned.

The goats being tended by this Masai child in a world Wildlife Fund project in Tanzania encourages the locals to develop and strengthen what they already practice.

*'People's Protest' image by the
Purari Action Group,
Papua-New Guinea*

Off to the banks of the Austrian Danube now, for a similar victory. In the winter of 1984, thousands camped for nights in sub-arctic temperatures in the Vienna Woods to protest against the construction of Austria's tenth hydro-electric plant at Hainburg. The plan involved damming the Danube and diverting its waters into a canal through the 8000-hectare Hainburg forest. This would stop the natural flooding of the woodland, an annual phenomenon which sustained a unique habitat popularly known as the 'Amazon of Europe'. This boggy forest, with its oaks, poplars and great willows was a refuge for all kinds of rare and unusual species, including sea eagles, black storks, otters, tree frogs, tortoises, orchids and water chestnuts. For years the woods had been at the top of a list of possible sites for Austria's first National Park, a major designated amenity for wildlife and visitors. But it had been scheduled instead for demolition by virtual drought.

Leading the protestors was the World Wildlife Fund. It invested over £$\frac{1}{2}$ million-worth of donations from all over the world to safeguard the Danube Wetlands. It was up against the state-owned Austrian power companies, the leading trade unions and the government itself. On the Wednesday before Christmas the authorities sanctioned what the national and international press called 'Austria's day of shame'. Eight hundred police used dogs and truncheons to evict the peaceful protestors from the forest, arresting forty and injuring many more. Tension was high. One WWF spokesman made the accusation that the government 'would put us all in concentration camps if they could'. The numbers of protestors increased dramatically day by day. At night the wood looked like a map of the winter Austrian sky, with the lights of a thousand campfires twinkling in the darkness.

An injunction was sought by the WWF in the Austrian and the European courts to stop the development on the grounds that it contravened two international wildlife and wetland treaties of which Austria was a signatory. Public and press pressure mounted, tension boiled over to the point when suddenly the government suspended the programme and initiated a complete review of the proposals. In the New Year, the project was cancelled. The Danube will not be dammed. The Vienna Woods are saved. The site has now been put forward by the IUCN as a World Heritage Site, registered for international protection.

The important thing is that it wasn't just protest action that won the day, but the combination of this with a reappraisal of the project's economic logic. The dam would have supplied an extra 3.6% of Austria's energy demands, but as the protestors pointed out, Austria already produced far more electricity than it ever needed or could sell. If the Danube development had not been stopped it would have supplied a development need which did not exist.

The developers had been caught out dancing in economic circles. Not only would the project have been the last waltz for the Vienna Woods but it would have led to the poisoning of the water supply to upwards of 250,000 local residents. It turned out that the biological processes of the riverine forest not only produced a habitat for wonderful wild plants and wildlife but also played a critical role in purifying the local water supply. Saved from destruction, the Vienna Woods could breathe once more, and continue their vital work of keeping the Danube clean.

PEOPLE POWER

How can we create jobs, banish unemployment, encourage investment and revitalize local economies if we're not going in for integrated development programmes? Maybe, a revolution is needed – power in the hands of the people to shake things up a bit?

We need violent revolutions like we need more nuclear weapons – not at all. However, there is another way . . . a revolution of attitudes and approaches to the problems of development. It's proper 'people power' and involves putting the impetus for development in the hands of the people themselves. It comes under a variety of names – 'bottom-up', rather than 'top-down' development . . . 'development from within' . . . 'local-level development' . . . 'self-help' and 'community development'. A certain amount of cautious but limited backing to this approach has come from bodies as august as the World Bank, the UNA, Oxfam, the British Overseas Development Authority, the English Development Commission, and a whole host of national and local governments, agencies, authorities and even private enterprise.

Developments based on people power, initially require research into what people want and need, what help to give them, what potential resources are and how they can be utilized, marketed and sustained for future use. People-powered development requires three other things: expert advice, tools and technology for action; education for local people and education of 'developers' about local needs and circumstances, and investment.

People power turns the traditional formula used for encouraging development on its head. It centres on the local community, making people not the objects of development programmes devised by others, but the active agents of projects they themselves have helped to devise, and which are suited to their direct needs. 'Helping people to help themselves' is the old slogan, but it has very practical and sound applications, and an environmental validity. Community involvement would not sanction a project that threatened the environment upon which it depended.

People Power is democratic with a difference. It encourages positive thinking and activity on the part of those who are so often at the butt-end of the planner's vision. It's less imperialistic, less colonialist, less ethnocentric, less patronizing in its approach to the basic problems of underdevelopment, poverty and sustainable resource use. It taps the power and potential for sustainable growth and responsible action and it can satisfy the hunger for a better deal and a bigger say that lies within us all.

Those of us in the First World with our sophisticated technology, advanced systems of education and wealth, have for too long thought we knew better than anyone else what was good for the Third World, for the 'undeveloped', and for the poor among ourselves. A quick resumé of the catalogue of disasters that have accompanied that attitude, from the Sahel to Bhopal would put much 'top-down' development firmly in its place: in the rear-end of history.

'Small is beautiful' ... clean, fresh water on tap from a newly-installed water pump in an Indian village.

Integrated crop development.
Underplanting rubber trees
with tea means a double crop, a
healthy, mixed habitat and a
stable soil.

The 'people power' approach has suffered from some false starts – inadequate
support, and penny-pinching funding from governments and commercial organizations. But that tide is at last beginning to turn. Two international organizations already leading the field include Oxfam and the Intermediate Technology
Group. Oxfam has discovered that for aid and investment in overseas development programmes to really be effective they have to be people-centred, drawing
on local initiative and local potential as much as possible. In Oxfam's experience,
most of the development projects that come only from 'above' – from governments, international organizations and relief agencies – tend to fail.

So, in many countries Oxfam now provides a down-to-earth advice and
grass-roots field service to local communities, with the promise of grant-aid for
projects which have potential and involve the people. A vast caseload includes
projects as diverse as: a community forestry development scheme in the
deforested Shivapuri Area of Nepal; a water harvesting scheme in the badly
eroded village lands of Yatanga on the edge of the Sahel in Africa and an

agricultural development programme in the Seraro area of Ethiopia. Oxfam also acts internationally with other aid agencies to put pressure on the big development funders like the World Bank, the UN's Food and Agricultural Organization and Development Programme, to change their approach. Through campaigns like 'Weather Alert', the 'Campaign for Real Aid' and 'Hungry for Change' they have even been able to secure financial backing for community-based schemes from both the big funders and the general public at large.

The Intermediate Technology Group was set up in 1965 to put into practice the ideas contained in Schumacher's *Small is Beautiful: An Economics as if People Mattered.* Schumacher advocated Third World development based upon a local approach, using technology on a human scale. His 'intermediate technology' represented a happy medium between a sickle and a combine harvester. Since its inception the Intermediate Technology group has designed, developed, tested and installed a wide range of appropriate tools and equipment for use by local groups in the Third World. In addition, when they install a wind-pump, set up a water harvesting project or design a food-processing unit they don't just set it up and walk away. They teach people how to use, manage and repair their equipment, market their produce and use the new technology to make themselves more self-reliant. Their engineers, economists and development advisers have stimulated successful grass-roots projects in over sixty countries and provided valuable technical advice to other major charities and aid agencies. One single wind-pump for example, designed and set up by Intermediate Technology at Kaikor in Kenya, serves the irrigation and drinking water needs of some 4000 nomads, and can be repaired and maintained by the Kenyans themselves. Without water, they and their cattle would die. They have water, food, and a development fitted to their circumstances, meeting their defined needs and enhancing their traditional livelihood, without in any way threatening their environment.

Some Third World development projects go even further than this by involving the local community itself in the actual design of the project. One such small-scale village based development has been set up in the village of Minigo in Tanzania. Minigo is one of thousands of typical villages in sub-Saharan Africa where the soil has become depleted through over-grazing, over cropping and erosion. The ground became unable to hold the valuable water from the mountains which gave it fertility: it just flowed across the land to be lost in the depths of Lake Victoria. By the 1970s things were getting right out of hand. There was no grass for the cattle, no vegetables, maize or millets for food or trade, and no other produce which they could sell to buy food. The villagers had started to rely upon cassava, a 'hunger-crop' which grows easily and stores well, but contains few vitamins, protein or minerals. Faced with malnutrition and the complete devastation of their village and its working environment, the villagers decided to act. Taking their destiny into their own hands they undertook a village appraisal, a diagnosis of their problems and an assessment of possible alternative solutions.

They decided on an irrigation development scheme to capture and harvest the water lost in run-off. In 1981 they started to dig canals on their land and with grant-aid and technological advice from Oxfam installed solar-powered electric pumps to lift water from Lake Victoria into the field plots. By 1984, the pumps were in operation and the villagers had commenced a new crop regime, growing onions, tomatoes and cabbage for village consumption and trade. A feasibility study had demonstrated that the new system would provide energy, water and food within one single integrated package, would improve the quality of the soil and secure an income of at least £100 a year for each family which participated in the scheme. The project is not without its problems, but it has great promise. Oxfam believe it could be a model for similar development schemes on a human scale across Africa. Its greatest capital is its human resource, the fact that the people who till the soil decided upon their own needs, worked out their own scheme, and then put their backs into it with heavy manual labour, to make it work. The process allowed the people a say in their own development, educating them into the art of the possible, increasing their own self-reliance, giving them community power, people power . . . and also economic power.

Under-development, a declining local economy and environmental dereliction, is a problem which affects not just the Third World but the developed world too. Ironically in the 1980s, the areas of Britain and Europe which experienced the very first impact of development, via the industrial revolution, are now the worst hit by an industrial recession which has been biting deeper and deeper since

Hebden Bridge, in the Pennines, is a cast-off of the Industrial Revolution, but now old mills and workhouses are being brought back to life by local development projects.

the end of the Second World War. But even in the worst affected areas like Scotland and the north-east of England, great spirit and resolve can still be found at grass-roots community level. All the signs of a fight-back, of people power, are there. But like Minigo, these need fostering and nurturing, just like plants grown from the roots, if appropriate development is to grow and flourish.

One desolate place in the developed world where some seeds of hope have already been sown by the local community is in the English southern Pennines, lying between the great industrial conurbations of Manchester and Leeds. Here is a curious combination of dramatic countryside, rolling moors and steep-sided valleys, and industrial settlement, of row upon row of smoky, terraced houses, old textile mills and railway lines. Its village communities were founded upon the textile industry, a development which is now long dead and gone, but which has left a legacy of distinctive landscape features, industrial archaeological ruins and tumbling textile mills. These mills loom large on the landscape, providing a visual warp to the weave of life that still lies within the terraced houses and the cobbled streets. But as the last remnants of the textile industry disappeared in the 1970s, so too the villages started to empty; unemployment became rife; and the whole area began to assume a run-down appearance. The valleys of the South Pennines, starved of development, of investment, of initiatives and of official support or enthusiasm for regeneration, began to fall into rack and ruin. There was a lot of talk about development and of the potential attractiveness of the area's scenic and industrial heritage for tourism and small-scale business activity, but no action.

In the late seventies, a group of volunteers, frustrated by this inaction, and appalled by the dereliction and sense of hopelessness which had been installed by official indifference, set up a trust, Pennine Heritage, to stem the tide of decline. The trust embarked on an ambitious programme of restoring buildings, undertaking landscape improvements and promoting the virtues of the area to the outside world. Work started with the conversion of a building threatened with demolition, Birchcliffe Chapel in Hebden Bridge. They raised enough money to rebuild it and convert it into an office and conference centre for local community and business groups. Other projects followed: the conversion of a Sunday School into a residential hostel; a tourism project, drawing attention to the area's canal and railway heritage; a Pennine Magazine for residents and outsiders that captured a readership of 35,000; a network to organize courses and conferences and to market the area; a taskforce to re-build stone walls, clear footpaths and restore wildlife habitats; and the conversion of two massive empty textile mills into industrial and craft workshops.

Pennine Heritage is really only at the very beginning of its own development. But its achievements are already quite remarkable. Buildings that were falling to the ground are back in active use. There is activity where once there was apathy. There is work where before there was nothing: hundreds of jobs are being created. There is investment; over $£\frac{1}{4}$ million raised from government bodies, charitable trusts and the private sector. Visitors, many of them from the USA and other countries, are bringing money into the area. And there is a new mood of co-operation and a sense of mutual endeavour among the local authorities and other bodies in the area actively concerned with the future of the area.

One of the models for the self-help community approach to development which is apparent in the Pennine Heritage scheme is the Mondragon Co-operative experiment in the Basque provinces of Northern Spain. Here, producer co-operatives have been in business for over thirty years, generated 19,000 jobs, and uniquely involve the workers in an investment and profit-sharing scheme which effectively guarantees good industrial relations. There is a total of ninety-six industrial co-operatives, seven agricultural, one consumer co-op with a supermarket and seventy-eight shops, and forty-four education, sixteen housing and four support co-operatives. They even have their own bank to provide development capital and re-invest the savings of the workers in their own

Shuttle launch July 1985 – massive investment – but to what end?

community. At Mondragon, the needs of the community and the environment in which the community is based have been given priority over the need to make money. But money is made, with surpluses, averaging £40 million per annum. The profits are re-invested into the locality as a hedge against recession and to maintain a diversity of development options.

Mondragon preserves a strong local grass-roots sense of communal identity with an upland environment, the foothills of the Pyrenees, which formerly had the same problems of decline, remoteness and environmental dereliction which the people of the Pennines encountered. The success of Mondragon owes much to one man, the local priest, Father Jose Maria Ariznendi, who spearheaded its establishment and formulated its constitution. But at the end of the day, without the determination, pride and committment of the local people, identifying closely with their local environment and the desire to build a prosperous community within that environment Mondragon would not have been possible. In this case, people-power involved taking full command of their locality, their own destiny.

In the UK today there are now over 1000 co-operatives operating on lines similar to those established by early profit-sharing enterprises like the Scott Bader Commonwealth. Between them these local co-operatives employ some 8000 people, a total which, at current growth rates, could rise to 50–100,000 employees by 1990. Their survival rate is in general better than that of equivalent privately-owned small businesses, and this is largely due to the ethos of working together for the common good, which co-operatives engender, and to the support of regionally-based Co-operative Development Agencies and local enterprise boards. This revitalized co-operative movement is still in its early days. It has become known as the Third Sector Economy. It points us towards a new age of development, work and responsibility. The co-operatives, as small-scale, locally responsive units, have a critical part to play in ushering in that Third Age, a new era which is not damned by the industrial mega-monsters of the past and the death rattle of out-dated ambitions. A manual for work, development, employment and 'progress' in any Third World Age which follows the inevitable stagnation and collapse of post-industrial western society has yet to be written. But its tools can only be forged by the experience and example of people power. The larger development agencies, the big banks, the World Bank, the International Monetary Fund and even goverment development bodies should be channelling a larger share of their cash and support towards these local initiatives. Investment at the grass-roots will alone stimulate development appropriate to local needs and wishes.

One of the exciting developments in people power is the growth of local self-help groups in developing countries, assisted by non-government organizations. Organizations like the Grameen Bank in Bangladesh have opened up cheap credit for local projects in the belief that access to rural credit for small farmers has greater impact than grants from aid agencies. The big problem is how to distribute funds to the right people at the right time in a way that doesn't throw them into confusion or force them to accept our ideas and technology that wouldn't suit their local needs. Local self-help structures like the Grameen Bank have helped show how this can be done. There are similar examples all over the world. The Popular Education movement in Venezuela is helping to start micro-businesses in manufacturing and services in the hill-side slums of Caracas or among poor farmers – the campesinos – high up in the Andes mountains. The Near East Council of Churches is promoting carpenters' co-operatives in the Gaza Strip, while the YWCA is helping to start small enterprises with women in refugee camps on the West Bank.

The sad thing is that it is easy to raise billions for big flash, First World-style projects which may be as useful as a cathedral in a desert. But raising money for more alternative ideas in the middle of Bangladesh or up the Venezuelan Andes is not so easy. Will the local people administer the money properly? Are they honest? Can they cope? These are the kind of questions aid administrators ask about self-help schemes at grass-roots level. It's a pity the big-project contractors and planners who may flatten a forest or drown a whole valley aren't questioned so closely.

Unfortunately, where the real progress is, at the grass-roots, appearances aren't so impressive . . . who gets a thrill from seeing two bullocks pulling a plough in the middle of the bush in Ghana? But such projects use modern agri-forestry techniques, in the right way at low cost, and effectively combat world hunger, however boring they may look!

Interesting or not, it is surely preposterous that mega-monstrous projects, the dams in Brazil, Malaysia, India, Thailand, large nuclear power programmes in oil-rich countries, trans-continental tunnels, and a host of other elephantine development programmes continue to swallow up massive amounts of capital investment and grant-aid. Because of this at the local level, where development really matters and where the proper beneficiaries of development are to be found, projects and project leaders are starved of capital. It's all out of balance, where conservative developmental thinking has its priorities wrong.

There is a big future in learning to think small – but are we big enough yet to change our ideas and our ways of working to do it?

7 A RACE TO THE END

BOMBS AWAY

The nuclear bomb and the population 'bomb' represent the greatest dangers facing humanity and the environment today. One is sitting there, ready and waiting to be dropped, while the other, despite some recent modifications, just keeps ticking away. The explosive power of each has the capacity to undermine the life-support systems of *Spaceship Earth* for all time, placing us on an orbit of permanent ruin and desolation, from which there will be little chance of recovery.

We're going to zoom in on some stark figures and bleak landscapes, eliminate a few popular misconceptions, and have a quick look over the edge of an abyss opening out before us.

We also take time out to visit a playground, a place of human theatre. A time to play, and an endless supply of eager and talented players. But do they, and we, really know just what we're playing with?

WELCOME TO THE WORLD

Today, like every day since that first morning of the world, the sun is shining somewhere on the planet. As its yellow rays and red tip appear on the horizon of Spaceship Earth, we welcome aboard another 200,000 fresh and shining new faces, happily joining us at the global breakfast table. There's nothing more beautiful than new birth, new life, to brighten up the dulling and dimming of old age.

The pure pleasures of parenthood are relative. It's OK if the new additions are welcome and you've got the resources to share round some extra bodies, to keep them going and growing. To the planet, parenthood is only manageable when the same conditions apply. For those 200,000 new people every day have to be fed, washed and clothed. Their bottoms have to be kept clean, their waste disposed of, their minds educated, their hands found gainful employment, and ultimately their remains have to be returned to the womb of the earth.

The production line of civilization deploys a cycle of attendants: midwife, doctor, dentist, teacher, lecturer, bank manager, insurance agent, farmer, manufacturer, energy producer, surgeon, pension manager and mortician. High output on the production line, and everyone's kept busy. The Gross National Product, which is an economic measure of that activity, is kept buoyant and growing. It also keeps the politicians happy and allows them to keep popping down the political pep pills and propping up the opinion polls.

Right *Will the future for this Peruvian family be as happy?*

Below *Masai mother and child, Kenya. Meanwhile, across the border in Ethiopia and the Sudan, world attention has focused on millions of children dying of starvation.*

It's bad news for the planet, however, and for the international balance of people and resources upon which all economic and political stability ultimately rests. It's certainly bad news if there's starvation, because of poor distribution of resources. But for many of the 200,000 newcomers, if starvation doesn't get them, unemployment and discontent certainly will. By the time each one of them is twenty, an extra 750 million people will have been added to the world's potential dole queues.

If we offer the new faces at the global breakfast table a guarantee of life at all, freedom from hunger, disease and annihilation by war, do we offer them a reasonable quality of life? Take the case of the UK, one of the world's richest countries, experiencing all the benefits of the leisure and wealth of the new white-hot high technology, lots of oil, gas and coal, surpluses in food and a commanding world trade position. But in the 1980s it is a country with one of the world's worst dole queues. That's not so hot and healthy, particularly if you are unemployed and live in a declining inner city. The cities are the unemployment and dereliction blackspots. The darkening of city lifelines and skylines seems to go hand in hand with the advance of the post-industrial, high technology dream. It took unemployment in Britain fourteen years to double from its 1957 level of 400,000, but less than six years to double again, and only two and a half years to double yet again by 1985. It presents another time-bomb of trouble and strife. Out of work, out of money, it's a pretty raw deal for the youngsters that Britain brings daily to the world's breakfast table. What kind of quality of life can *they* expect?

The UK is also overcrowded, and that too undermines the quality of life. Imagine if one particularly sunny day, a national holiday was suddenly declared, and we all downed tools and departed for the seaside to enjoy the sunshine. Our delight would be short-lived. All the cars, lorries and coaches on the coast and country roads would very quickly grind to a halt. There would be not more than 25 millimetres of breathing space between each stationary vehicle. The congestion to the coast would be unimaginable. Not everyone would go to the coast it is true, but you don't have to declare a national holiday, to know that there are too many cars and too many people around to ensure easy access for all to the freedom of the sea and a decent paddle once we all got there. If the present population of the UK stood on all the available British coastline, they'd have to stand on one foot because they'd have four inches of paddling room each! Overcrowding congests and degrades life not just in the cities but also in the seaside resorts and the diminishing areas of the countryside to which we have access.

Overcrowding on its own is not the cause of Britain's problems. There are many causes, most of them political. But in our case, high-density living aggravates the problems of dereliction and massive unemployment and the politicians refuse to deal with them effectively. A constantly-increasing population on an island, where the density of population is four times that of China, puts immense pressure on the resources and the ability to manage the problems. The people of Britain eat, on average, three times as much, and consume forty times the amount of industrial products and fossil fuels as their Third World counter-   *Bora Camp, Wollo, Ethiopia*

parts. The UK depends on imports for 50% of its food and animal feed, and for a wide variety of raw materials except energy supplies – and despite massive energy stocks of oil, gas and coal, some of these are imported. Britain's constant balance of payments problem is directly related to the fact that its population is wildly in excess of its available resources.

It has been estimated that the optimum ideal population, socially and economically, for Britain is 30 million. That means there is a current uneconomic surplus of 26 million – we're right over the top of what we can afford to support. There's not a lot we can do, or would wish to do, about our current totals, but we could certainly plan for a future which takes this figure as a sustainable basis for living. The entire population could be more self-sufficient in basic foods, and there would be less profit in the degrading and possibly dangerous produce of factory-farming. Many of the shortages in educational resources and housing would disappear. Everyone's means could be maintained at a high capital level, and every adult could enjoy the luxury of owning and running a lean-burn motor vehicle. The UK's overseas trade and payment balances would be healthier. The people of Britain would no longer be such a drain on the world's supply of natural resources, and would be less vulnerable to the swings, roundabouts and roller-coaster effects of world economic fortunes.

The good news is that the population growth rate in Britain is already falling. Rising standards of living, a public-spirited concern about overpopulation, the higher level of material comforts which are possible with smaller families, family planning, improved means of contraception, education and even house design, have all contributed to an average rate of 1.7 childbirths per family. It's good news elsewhere too. Between 1980–85, the average rate of childbirth in Austria, Belgium, Finland, West Germany, Luxembourg, Netherlands, Sweden and Switzerland was down below 1.6. As popular responsibility has grown, population growth has slowed down. A continuation of current rates of childbirth in Britain alone, with proper forward-looking, pre-natal, pre-fatal, family planning policies, the UK's population could be on sustainable target levels by AD 2080. But there are other First World countries, particularly France, where there is a growing counter-trend, a pro-natal lobby, and some leading politicians are jumping on a bulge bandwagon. Before they get too carried away, let's dispose of a few of the much simplified 'popular' misconceptions on which more traditional pro-natal parties base their arguments:

Misconception One: *'Birth rates throughout the world are declining at the fastest rate in history. Concern about population is one of the biggest 'con'. tricks of all time.'*

The real 'con'. trick is complacency. The fact is, that with 35% of the world's population now under the age of 15, the next generation of parents has already been born. And even if birthrate was reduced to replacement levels (two surviving children for every fertile woman) the world population would still continue to grow for the next 60 years. Whatever we do, bar a catastrophic world war or a pan-global epidemic of Aids or some other disease, the world's population will be 6.1 billion by the turn of the century and 8.2 billion by 2025. The life-support systems of *Spaceship Earth* are already under immense pressure. With that lot on board, the whole thing could still crash: chaos could take over the helm of a system right out of control. The challenge the earth's children would inherit in 2080 would include the need to reduce population levels by drastic means, and as resources are depleted, the problems of coping with mass starvation and colossal environmental catastrophe, Those disasters would dwarf anything ever seen to date. Unless we stop now the deceiving and some of the misconceiving the problems for them will be impossible to control, let alone prevent.

Misconception Two: *'Population growth is a result of poverty, not the cause.'*

It's just not that simple. Of the world's thirty-six least-developed countries, twenty-eight have reached, or are starting to reach the dangerously critical world ratio of one person per acre of arable crop land. The population of all those countries is set to double within the next thirty years. Even this is a conservative estimate – censuses in many Third World countries are somewhat casual affairs. These are countries which also face rising problems of poverty. And although

Chinese twins – a bonus under the national one family, one-child policy.

population growth does not directly cause their poverty, it contributes to it, accentuating it, making recovery from the depths of poverty that much more difficult and less manageable. China has shown that by drastically reducing its rate of population growth, it has been able to spread a higher share of the benefits of economic improvements among fewer people. There is correspondingly less pressure all round on land, resources, means of waste disposal and the lives of its new generation of one-child families.

Misconception Three: '*Development is the best contraceptive.*'

This arises at least in part from the knowledge that the eight countries in the world where women tend, on average, to have two or less children during their active reproductive lives are amongst the most developed in the world. The women enjoying wealthy, liberated lives are all in the $10,000-plus per capita GNP bracket.

But in those Third World countries where there has been rapid development, population has not fallen. Over the last twenty years, Kenya for example, has pursued policies of massive economic expansion and social advance. Yet its population is growing faster than that of any other country in the world, and is expected to double within the next seventeen years. That means there will be an extra 20 million mouths to feed and jobs to find, in a land of which only 18% is considered arable, yet 80% of the population is dependent on agriculture. Even in the developing countries at the other end of the GNP stakes, where oil is lubricating the local economy above the $20,000 per capita level, things are almost as bad. The population of Quatar is expected to double in thirty years; United Arab Emirates in thirty-two years; and Kuwait in twenty-one years.

No, a high cash flow, lots of economic growth, wealth and development, do not necessarily act as contraceptives. 'Money up, birth rate down' is not a valid premise – a bitter pill which many, many developers and economists find hard to swallow. In Egypt, many of the hopes of the development theorists were pinned to the success of the Aswan Dam project. This turned out to be an economic white elephant and an ecological catastrophe. But even if it had been a success, with Egypt's current rate of population growth, at least another five such developments would be needed to provide enough irrigated land and energy to cater for the basic nutritional needs of its people.

Successful development and successful population control depend upon one another. In the control of poverty they go hand in hand. If there is no development, family-planning is ineffective, and vice-versa. Many Third World countries cannot afford to wait around for development while their populations explode, putting more and more pressure on existing, undeveloped resources.

Given that First World interference technologies, ideas and medicines are behind the recent rapid population growth in many Third World countries, the First World has a responsibility to help solve the problems. This can be done with development advice and family-planning assistance, but also by example. The countries of the First World, Europe and the US, must also reject the pro-natal lobby and keep its own population levels at replacement levels or below. They must attack their own high level of per-capita resource consumption, and work towards a fairer distribution of resources. They must be prepared to de-develop, to bring their economic systems, particularly patterns of consumption, into line with the realities of ecology and the limits of available resources.

The threat of the 'Population Bomb' first blew up in the 1960s. Our success in curbing population growth in the First World is a positive indication that we can control at least some of the excesses of *Homo sapiens*. There is hope for the future but the bomb is not defused yet. Unless we continue to wind down, and control the rate of explosion engineered by modernization and economic growth, there will be no real hope of sustainable economic progress and recovery anywhere in the world. The points made by Paul and Anne Erlich on the relationship between population resources and environment in 1970 are as valid now as they were then. These are their six points of no return:

1. Considering present technology and behaviour patterns our planet is grossly overpopulated.

2. The large absolute number of people and the rate of population growth are major hindrances to solving human problems.

3. The limits of human capability to produce food by conventional means have very nearly been reached. Problems of supply and distribution already have resulted in roughly half of humanity being undernourished or malnourished. Some 10–20 million people are starving to death annually.

4. Attempts to increase food production further will tend to accelerate the deterioration of our environment, which in turn will eventually *reduce* the capacity of the earth to produce food. It is not clear whether environmental decay has now gone so far as to be essentially irreversible; it is possible that the capacity of the planet to support human life has been permanently impaired. Such technological 'successes', as automobiles, pesticides, and inorganic nitrogen fertilizers are major causes of environmental deterioration.

5. There is reason to believe that population growth increases the probability of a lethal world-wide plague and of a thermo-nuclear war. Either could provide an undesirable 'death rate solution' to the population problem; each is potentially capable of destroying civilization and even of driving humankind to extinction.

6. There is no technological panacea for the complex of problems composing the population-food-environment crisis, although technology, properly applied in such areas as pollution abatement, communications, and fertility control can provide massive assistance. The basis solutions involve dramatic and rapid changes in human *attitudes*, especially those relating to reproductive behaviour, economic growth, technology, the environment, and conflict resolution.[15]

Basically it all boils down to, 'whatever your cause, it's a lost cause without population control'.

CHILDREN OF THE FUTURE

No-one who experiences the joys of parenthood likes to think they're contributing to a population bomb. New-born babies and little children are lovely – even if at times they do behave like little bomblets, messing up our tidy lives and drawing pictures on manuscripts for *Turning the Tide*. The pleasure they give is on the whole quite matchless: all that tumbling energy, bright-eyed innocence and new life, giving fresh hope for us all and for our futures.

But look at the world we bring them into. How the armies of sometimes so-called democratic governments, 'Defenders of the People', 'Freedom Fighters', revolutionary guards, counter-revolutionaries and government troops can wake up in the morning and go to sleep at night, with the blood of innocent children on their hands and in their consciences, is beyond the imagination of any loving parents. Yet murdered children are a daily part of life in the battlefields and guerilla jungles of the Middle East, South-East Asia, Africa and Central America. And in the darkest corners of the most depressing urban environments that the Western World has spawned, there lurk twisted human fiends, the products of developed society at its sickest, who wait to prey, to exert their violence, their sickness, upon the innocence of little children.

But a greater problem than these in numerical terms is the ever-expanding market in child-labour – children being forced to become instruments in the new processes of profiteering and over-ambitious, officially-encouraged economic growth. In 1980, after much hesitation, the UN's Economic and Social Council decided to act upon the abuse of child labour across the globe. They set up a working group on child slavery and came up with some startling and disturbing findings. In its conclusions, the group's report states that:

Child labour in Britain was outlawed decades ago. It is still common practice to put children to work elsewhere in the world today.

Opposite
Above *Children in the First World – with time to play and be young.*

Below *Childhood for this North Indian boy is spent tanning buffalo hides for leather.*

'It had been widely thought that the problem of slavery was largely obsolete. Unfortunately, it has turned out to be nothing of the kind; slavery-type practices remain very widespread throughout the world: bond-service for debt, sale of children, the prostitution of others, traffic in women (white and coloured), exploitation of child labour.'

Compare this with the idealism of the Declaration of the Rights of the Child passed in 1959 by the UN General Assembly. This formally ruled that 'The child should in no case be caused or permitted to engage in any occupation or employment which would prejudice his or her health or education or interfere with his or her physical, mental or moral development.'

Compare that with everyday reality in many countries of the world. As if we needed any further education on this matter, here's a quick selection of entries into the ABC of world child-labour abuse. It makes difficult and disturbing reading, and the sums add up to a multiplication of shame:

A *is for Africa, with a per capita GNP of $783 and a population ready to double in twenty-three years.*
Some estimates suggest that as many as 16 million African children under the age of thirteen are compelled to work. In traditional African society, working children are an economic fact of life, but how much of this new figure represents abuse and exploitative practices through imported production-line processes?

B *is for Bolivia, with a per capita GNP of $601, and a population ready to double inside twenty-six years.*
Maria is a daughter of Bolivia, a child in a Christian society, a country with rich resources and low population density. She is seven, and was sold on the market for £25. In Bolivia and other developing countries like Chile, Brazil, Thailand and the Maghreb children are often given in payment for a debt entered into by the family or even just to have one mouth less to feed.

C *is for Columbia, with a per capita GNP of $1334, and a population ready to double in thirty-five years.*
The national committee of the *International Year of the Child* drew attention to the groups of waifs left to their own devices. Some children are employed for eight hours a day in mines 280 metres underground.

I *is for India, with a per capita GNP of $253, and a population ready to double in thirty-three years.*
In some parts of Bombay 24.7% of children began work between the ages of six and nine and 48.4% between the ages of ten and twelve. The remaining 26.9% entered the labour market between the ages of thirteen and fifteen. A lot of the work they do is intensive industrial labour.

I *is also for Italy with a per capita GNP of $1390 and a population ready to double in 495 years.*
According to government statistics, 8.18% of the victims of industrial accidents

were children or adolescents. Italy has the dubious distinction of registering the youngest disability pensioner in the world – a young boy who lost his hand while working in a saw mill. There are laboratorie in Naples, sinister workshops without windows, where thousands of women and children work in the dark, under conditions certainly no better than those in Bangkok or Delhi.

P *is for Pakistan with a per capita GNP of $349 and a population ready to double in twenty-five years.*

The children of Pakistan have made their country the fourth largest exporter of carpets in the world. There are thought to be 1.5 million boys and girls who work at carpet weaving, many of them are under the age of six.

R *is for the Republic of Korea with a per capita GNP of $1720 and a population ready to double in forty-one years.*

At the bottom of the employment ladder are girls barely twelve or thirteen who machine shirt collars and cuffs for a few cents an hour, seated all day on hard, wooden slats in poorly-lit hovels.

T *is for Thailand with a per capita GNP of $769 and a population ready to double within thirty-five years.*

Between 100 and 200 children under sixteen arrive in Bangkok by train every morning to look for work. A shop in Bangkok receives and sells about 20,000 children a year, about a quarter of them under the age of sixteen.

T *is also for Taiwan with a per capita GNP of $2360 and a population expected to double inside thirty-eight years.*

Thousands of girls between the ages of twelve and fifteen work in the small industrial enterprises of South Taiwan. For a working day of 12–14 hours, the monthly wage is $50. Strikes are prohibited by law. Safety measures and social security payments are practically non-existent.

W *is for Working Children of the World.*

According to the World Bank, the number of children in the working population is 17 per 1000 in Asia, 6 per 1000 in South America and one per 1000 in Europe and the USA. Not for these children the delights of childhood, the freedom of play, and the chance to learn about more than working for adults and scratching a living. Because most of the victims are in the developing countries, those of us living in the 'high moral' climes of the First World can easily condemn child-labour and consider it a problem remote from our lives and consciences. But is it? ... just go round your house counting the number of household items, clothing and electrical equipment made in those countries, especially Taiwan and Thailand. They may be products dreamed up by designers and marketed by salesmen, but the chances are, they're made by little children! There's dirt sticking to the fingers of us all. If this is what we do to our children, why are we welcoming them to the world's breakfast table? For the children we do welcome into the world we must at least be sure that we can offer them a chance to play, and a place along with every other species in a world with a future.

TO THE ABYSS AND BEYOND

From the play of little children to the play of adults. It's often said that the playing fields of yesterday are the war fields of tomorrow. Our next and penultimate port of call is one such playing field.

Our chosen playing field is a cricket ground. It could be anywhere in the world, India, New Zealand, the West Indies, even the Trobriand Islands in the South Pacific, but as our time is nearly up, it is in the heart of England. It is early evening and the evening sun casts a warm red light on the freshly-cut grass and great oaks around the ground. By the pavilion, beer is being served. And there's tea for those who want it. Yesterday's men are dozing in deck chairs with copies of

Cricket on a golden afternoon, timeless, civilized and calm ... far but not safe from the cares of the real world.

the Financial Times over their faces. You can see the headline on one 'Tension Rises in Middle East'. But there's no tension here. Just a warm atmosphere and an air of relaxed civilized calm. Somehow its civilization personified, the 'English Way of Life', and an evening peace, an ideal that so many have fought and died for.

Out on the ground, a world-class cricketer, playing a benefit match in aid of research into child leukaemia, strikes another easy six. There's a wave of applause around the ground. A church bell tolls and from the trees evening blackbirds sing . . . The crowd and the cricketers don't know it yet but three minutes ago, many thousands of miles away, in another part of the world, war has broken out. A few more minutes pass, and a few more runs are made . . . One of the cricketers is the

first to see it. All heads and eyes turn in stunned amazement and disbelief. In the distance, the object of their attention, a cloud of smoke, builds and billows into the atmosphere and spreads across the sky. There's not even time to panic, and nowhere to hide. Soon the flash comes, the earth rumbles, the sky darkens and the trees blaze. The pitch simply evaporates. There's no more scores to be made, all sides have been run out.

You're probably thinking, 'No, it's not real, not possible, it couldn't happen here.' Couldn't it? But in fact the greatest, most imminent threat to the forward passage of *Spaceship Earth*, the survival of the human species and the well-being of its environment, is without doubt Nuclear War. Since the beginning of its existence, the human species has always waged war upon itself. There's nothing new in that. What is new though, is our ability to wage a war which could annihilate not just individual human beings, but the entire human species, and with it, all life on earth and even the planetary environment upon which any chance of future life evolving must depend. This ability to bring on our own Armageddon is a relatively new twist to the evolution of the species – it's only thirty to forty years old.

The average fellow traveller on *Spaceship Earth* observes this theatre of the absurd, staged partly behind a curtain of secrecy, scientific jargon and military game-planning, with a detached, seemingly unconcerned eye, preferring to trust the arguments of the players and not think about the last act and the final curtain. But the play is almost over, and however distant we may think we are from it as individuals, as ordinary citizens, the fact is that we're pretty close. And if you look behind you right now you'll see that the strategists and the politicians have already bolted and barred most of the exits and they're busy setting fire to the fire-doors, the roof and the stage.

Over the short period during which we've had the capacity to destroy our environment within minutes, there have been a total of 1524 nuclear weapons tests. In the early days these were done above ground, in full view of foot-soldiers and luckless passers-by – in Nevada, on Maralinga, and in the Urals. Then, during the late fifties and early sixties, scientists from all over the globe expressed concern about the serious genetic disorders and cancers caused by above-ground nuclear explosions. Apart from the immediate dangers to people and the environment, these explosions were effectively building up a layer of radio-active particles in the earth's upper atmosphere which would drift back down to Earth in the decades lying ahead. Nuclear tests, it was discovered, also produce nitric oxides in the stratosphere, depleting the ozone layer and later returning to the earth as acid rain. When the bomb builders and politicians eventually became convinced that proximity to atomic or hydrogen bursts actually killed or radiated people and things well beyond the test site, and had an incurable effect on atmosphere stability, they moved everything underground. Most of today's bombs boom below the surface of the earth and the seas, having an incalculable effect upon the environments beneath our feet. Who knows what real long-term seismic stress, geological disturbances or even earthquakes are caused by underground nuclear testing? All we really know is that we don't know enough. And the people who think they do know, prefer to keep their knowledge to themselves, after all, the full truth might cost them their careers, their involvement in a rather well-paid industry. We do know a little though:

'Controlled nuclear explosions' underwater are known to have direct climatic effects. The French nuclear tests held in the South Pacific have had the effect of heating the ocean waters around the test sites. After tests, temperatures of 31–32°C have been reported during the cold season in the ocean waters between Tahiti and the Equator. It is known that a sudden warming of ocean currents above 28°C in these parts of the world causes cyclones. After the French tests in the late seventies and eighties, the islands around Tahiti and Muroroa Atoll suffered a sudden barrage of cyclones and tidal waves. Tahiti had never experienced a cyclone in living history. For the other islands in the South Pacific there had been no strong cyclones for over sixty years. These warmer ocean currents in the Pacific in 1983 have also been blamed for the winds which caused destructive rains and mud-slides, for reversing the equatorial trade winds, and for causing drought in Australia and Fiji. Throughout the 1980s, there has been no recorded incidence of volcanic activity to give a natural explanation to the mysterious warming of the ocean waters and the sudden appearance of those winds of death.

With the French, British and Americans all testing atomic warfare in the South Pacific, the area, by the 1980s, was hardly 'pacific'. It has become a playground for a war zone, the ultimate conclusion of which is the destruction of everything: a war on earth which without doubt would end all wars. In 1984 the nuclear warriors went one step further. The US fired a missile into space from Kwajalein Atoll just north of the Equator; its objective was to destroy a target launched into the stratosphere from California some 4000 miles away; its success heralded the possibility of war in space. The boundary between the living planet and outer space had been breached, and the human species had entered a new nuclear era: the age of Star Wars. It must be quite clear by this time that nuclear weapons work, yet there's a constant testing of nuclear weapons, an increasing drive to explore new ways of waging a war that can only have one conclusion. One explanation for this has been put forward from within the weapons industry. In 1985, the Director of the Lawrence Livermore Laboratory in the US, Roger Batzel, submitted his views to the US House of Representatives. He argued that a comprehensive test ban treaty would impair America's national security interests. 'Continued testing is necessary to maintain deterrence capability.' In other words the weapons are built to be used. If they cannot be used, this is terribly frustrating for the builders and the end-users, so instead they must be constantly tested and retested, and never left to lie around in stock-piles and go rusty . . . and also to confirm the need for more tests they have to conduct even more tests. According to our source:

> 'Nuclear tests have identified design problems and unanticipated effects of ageing which dramatically affected performance of certain devices, in some instances affecting a large fraction of the stock-pile. Major unexpected vulnerabilities were also revealed and safety was found to be reduced.'[16]

The logic is convoluted: they need tests of tests in order to testify to the efficiency of the tests and the inefficiency of no-tests! The implications of this curious piece of circular thinking don't bear thinking about.

Batzell also believes that a ban on testing would have a destabilizing effect, not just upon the international 'balance' of terror but upon the weapons-producing work-force ... 'Weapon design experts would inevitably leave the weapons programme because they could not verify their theoretical ideas with experiments. Those who stayed would gradually lose their sharpness.' Our hearts must bleed with their loss. With vested interests like this, no wonder there is no desire to stop testing, no desire to stop building more weapons. It's a wonder that they haven't been able to persuade their government of the need to conduct a small nuclear war somewhere in the world – 'testing only' of course – in order to further their job satisfaction and careers. Such irresponsible talk is, of course, only possible so long as the war for which their weapons are intended doesn't happen. Meanwhile they can at least spend their time devising and testing newer and even more wicked ways of conducting World War Three. A test ban would in Batzel's view 'prevent the exploration of new capabilities and new effects,' although he does generously concede that the destruction of cities requires 'no further research and development'.

Well that's reassuring. But what kind of level of destruction is envisaged for further research and development that cannot be conducted already. With a current total deployment of 50,000 nuclear warheads, many of them multiple, and each of them with a megatonnage and explosive power many times that of the

Opposite
Regular atmospheric and underground nuclear tests are irradiating our planet. If the weapons are ever used for their ultimate purpose, destruction would be rather less gradual.

Nuclear testing affects climate and earth movements around the world, and could trigger off a dust storm like this one in South Australia.

bombs which destroyed Hiroshima and Nagasaki, we are already in a position to conduct nuclear overkill. Even a mutually agreed or multi-lateral decision to halve the current weapons capability of the two main superpowers, the US and the USSR, would still leave us with the capacity to destroy civilization ten times over.

So why do they keep adding to the stock-piles? Why do the world's governments wish to spend a total of $750 billion in one year in armaments? Why does the World spend 20% more of its wealth in developing weapons designed to destroy life, than in instituting the health measures necessary to preserve life? What kind of a defence policy is it that puts a higher value on creating more and more unnecessary weapons of death than on sustaining the inner defences of the people, the provision of plentiful food, clean water and a healthy environment? What kind of cynical morality is involved when the metaphor used to communicate the successful explosion of the first-ever nuclear device that caused the death of hundreds of thousands of men, women and children is of 'babies satisfactorily born'?

The answer to these questions, an explanation of the psychology of overkill, is as old as evolution: it is the desire to be one ahead of the next individual, the desire to obtain competitive advantage. But in the nuclear club, the politics of strategic advantage take on a terminal dimension. The powers-that-be seem ready and willing to march us forward into a deliberate unknown, for the sake of advantage. The build-up of weapons on each side of the nuclear bull-ring is calculated on the basis that one power does the greatest possible damage before the inevitable and unstoppable retaliation bulldozes him in return. Yet both sides readily agree that in the end everyone gets destroyed. And if you're sitting on the fence in the middle, you'll get it too. All sides are now beginning to recognize that nuclear war is species and environmental suicide, the murder of the living planet. But still they carry us on into the abyss.

'Limited nuclear war', 'nuclear theatres', 'the game plan', 'controlled warfare', a 'limited nuclear scenario', 'strategic defence initiatives', 'star wars', and so on: these are the strategic concepts of the morally bankrupt. Their defence systems leave us defenceless; their nuclear-plated armouries, ostensibly built to protect 'A Way of Life', are nothing but an invitation to a 'Way of Death'.

The pro-nuclear and anti-nuclear lobbies are equally pessimistic about the outcome of the arms race: the whole thing has a terrible, even logical, inevitability. But whereas the anti-nuclear people campaign vigorously for radical disarmament to scale down the stock-pile, the pro-nuclear people believe there is no real turning back. The nuclear club talk endlessly about principles of disarmament, of parity and minimal systems of deterrence, but this is no more than public relations, pure theatre. As Professor Raymond Williams put it:

> 'their real politics and planning are not centred on these, but on an acceptance of the indefinite continuation of extreme crisis and extreme danger . . . For the real objective is neither disarmament nor parity, but temporary competitive advantage, within a permanent and inevitable danger.'[17]

And the whole time, while the politicians and diplomats bluster and blow, while they parry thrusts in Third World theatres of conventional war, while they field strategic challenges and take tea at summits, the vested interests, the nuclear scientists, the armourers and weapon-makers are all busy behind the scenes digging – ever-deeper into the gold-plated depthless nuclear trough. Disproportionate and rapidly-escalating levels of national and international finance are committed year upon year to maintaining and building upon the nuclear megatonnage which sustains the politics of strategic advantage. Funds are drained from essential services, from development aid, from poverty alleviation measures, from peaceful technologies to fill the ever-bulging fathomless pockets of the weapons-makers and their marketing men. Even research laboratories of once-great institutions of human learning are now largely sustained on a diet of capital from the ministries of defence. The best young scientific words of a generation have been turned into the tools of madmen to aid the design of ever and ever better and more and more horrific ways of terminating life on earth. The plough-shares of the future are being beaten not into swords but nuclear missiles, into laser devices and death rays for shooting down nuclear missiles from outer space. And to help offset the considerable costs of all this, new tools of destruction, both conventional and nuclear, are traded across the globe regardless of non-proliferation pacts, arms limitation treaties and the like. Officially or unofficially, every other year a new country amasses the technology to join the international nuclear club, to stake their individual share in the apocalypse.

So what happens when the end comes, when the earth rumbles and sky does fall on our heads? One possible scenario has been painted by an international group of respected atmospheric and planetary scientists, including among their number Paul Erlich and Carl Sagan. According to them an escalating large-scale nuclear war – the inevitable outcome of nuclear exchange on any scale – could end up with a world-wide nuclear winter. A brief and deadly summer of fireballs, ionizing radiation, and mushroom clouds reaching well into the stratosphere would be followed by the big freeze and the end of the world.

The theory of the nuclear winter has its dissidents; it can only be put to the test of experience, and cannot therefore be proved. But the weight of evidence now amassed has the backing of august international scientific bodies like the Royal Society of Canada, the International Union of Scientific Unions, and the National Research Council of the US National Academy of Sciences. The early findings of scientists and researchers reporting to these bodies have even been endorsed by senior Soviet military research establishments and the US Pentagon. And although there is disagreement and debate about the length, severity and ultimate effect on planetary life of such a winter, most agree with the evidence of a huge climatic change on earth, the likes of which the planet has never seen. The internal, on-board operating systems of *Spaceship Earth* would in such circumstances completely malfunction. All its life and life-support systems would, if they survived at all, never be the same again. This is the scenario we could look forward to:

- An exchange of significant fractions of the world's nuclear arsenals would incur mammoth explosions sending dust, radio-activity and various gases into the atmosphere. The explosions would ignite fires, burning cities, chemical installations, nuclear power stations, forests, fuel and grasslands in the nuclear countries.

- The fires would send plumes of gases and smoke many thousands of feet into the atmosphere. Within weeks, some of the dust, radio-activity and smoke would be carried by winds around the earth, remaining in the atmosphere for an indefinable period.

- Clouds of smoke and dust would spread around the northern hemisphere and possibly around and across the equator. In time these would settle on to the ground. Under the clouds, daylight would be reduced to twilight or even complete darkness – the nuclear night – for weeks to come.

- Temperatures on land would drop under the clouds of dust and smoke, and would not return to normal for possibly over a year. Large parts of the world would freeze, plants and seeds in the northern hemisphere not obliterated by the initial blasts and fallout would not grow for several months. Harvests would fail all over the north, and harvests in the south would be poor for years to come. Countless wild animals and plants, whole species and entire ecosystems of grassland and forest would be made extinct. Those that survived would be genetically impaired, and possibly sterile. Advanced agriculture would collapse, the soil would be poisoned for years to come. The subsequent epidemic diseases and starvation would wipe out millions more than had died from the war itself or its accompanying radiation.[18]

After nuclear winter, suffering would be on an astronomical and unmanageable scale.

The nuclear winter is only a theory. It may never happen. But the last thing we want is for that theory ever to be tested. So how do we avoid the final experiment? We begin at the beginning of nuclear technology itself, to heed the advice of Albert Einstein, whose discoveries did much to take us to the abyss, but who bitterly regretted the implications of his findings.

After hearing of the destruction of Nagasaki and Hiroshima at the end of World War Two, Einstein warned

'The unleashed power of the atom has changed everything except our way of thinking ... we need an essentially new way of thinking if mankind is to survive.'

A typhoon in the South Pacific as seen from space. A rise in typhoon activity in this part of the world has been linked with cycles of nuclear testing.

This must involve at least three broad changes of mind, three cut-off points from the Cro-Magnon thinking of the nuclear age. These have been set out by Raymond Williams as the primary 'Resources for a Journey of Hope'. The first of these requires that we stop thinking in terms of strategic advantage, economic exploitation, and unbound 'progress' for the sake of it. We must realize that the world consists of life and land forms bound together in a web of interdependence.

Destroy our environment and we destroy ourselves. Destroy ourselves and we destroy our environment.

Secondly we can no longer afford to tie ourselves down to the outmoded pursuit of constantly increased and increasing modes of production, both capitalist and socialist. Both lead to inhuman institutions which strive for constant advantage, within and between one another and against the institutions of others. In the process they exploit and destroy. We need to replace these modes with new livelihoods which are practical, self-managing and self-sustaining, which involve caring first for each other and our living world.

The third change involves working towards a whole way of life where not just scientific rationality and rational argument dictate the measure and worth of things, but ordinary emotions and instincts are taken into full account, and given an equal hearing. The deformed social order that has given us the possibility of a nuclear winter has for too long used 'rational' intelligence and calculated advantage to disguise actions which to most people are emotionally unacceptable and instinctively repulsive.[19] •

As for the weapons themselves, the ultimate creations of evolutionary advantage, which allow us to contemplate our own destruction, these must be completely destroyed. The only real solution is a complete, world-wide freeze on all research and development on weapons of mass destruction; a complete international ban on all nuclear testing; and an end to the trade in weapons and the raw

The aftermath of the first atomic bomb in Hiroshima over forty years ago – we've come a long way since then.

materials of the nuclear industry. Following this there must be negotiated deep cuts in the current stock-piles, deep cuts which can be verified by an international, post-nuclear commission of independent observers. Multi-lateral disarmament, unilateral disarmament, the procedure does not ultimately matter. All nuclear weapons must be placed on the table and put away for good before some awful accident or act of idiocy engulfs us all.

This is not wilful idealism — we have absolutely no choice; either we freeze deployment, development and testing *NOW*, and make a concerted effort to reduce the international nuclear temperature, or we freeze later, in the world's final winter. The choice we face has been admirably set out by Jonathan Schell in his *The Fate of the Earth*:

> 'Two paths lie before us. One leads to death, the other to life. If we choose the first path — if we numbly refuse to acknowledge the nearness of extinction, all the while increasing our preparations to bring it about — then we in effect become the allies of death, and in everything we do our attachment to life will weaken: our vision, blinded to the abyss that has opened at our feet, will dim and grow confused; our will, discouraged by the thought of trying to build on such a precarious foundation anything that is meant to last, will slacken; and we will sink into stupefaction, as though we were gradually weaning ourselves from life in preparation for the end. On the other hand, if we reject our doom, and bend our efforts toward survival — if we arouse ourselves to the peril and act to forestall it, making ourselves the allies of life — then the anaesthetic fog will lift: our vision, no longer straining not to see the obvious, will sharpen; our will, finding secure ground to build on, will be restored; and we will take full and clear possession of life again.
>
> One day — and it is hard to believe that it will not be soon — we will make our choice. Either we will sink into the final coma and end it all or, as I trust and believe, we will awaken to the truth of our peril, a truth as great as life itself, and, like a person who has swallowed a lethal poison but shakes off his stupor at the last moment and vomits the poison up, we will break through the layers of our denials, put aside our fainthearted excuses, and rise up to cleanse the earth of nuclear weapons.'[20]

8 THE GREEN HORIZON

A PROPHECY FULFILLED?

We are fast approaching the year 2000, the end of a century of unparalleled technological progress and seemingly limitless growth. But the pace and scale of this has introduced an imbalance within our environment which threatens the well-being of the planet and the very survival of humankind.

To tip the scales back we need some new ideas, new standards and new leaders who understand our responsibilities to the environment. Can such a vision, a new horizon for *Spaceship Earth*, be found in the political philosophies of the Green parties? Have their ideas finally found their time? In the new growth of the Green movement and their ideas are we witnessing the fulfillment of this old Indian prophecy?:

'When the earth has been ravaged and the animals are dying, a tribe of people from all races, creeds and colours will put their faith in deeds, not words, to make the land green again. They will be called 'Warriors of the Rainbow' – protectors of the environment.'

ON THE SHORELINE

Now in the final stages of our environmental journey we return to the shoreline where it all began to watch the turning of the tide.

The spot we've chosen is a beautiful one: Druridge Bay in Northumberland on the north-east coast of England. It's mostly unspoilt, and one of the largest stretches of sandy coastline on the shores of the great North Sea. It's a great place for coastal wildlife, particularly the birds. It's also a great place for a holiday, for relaxing your inner and outer defences, for playing with the children and like them going a bit wild, free as a bird, enjoying the sand, waves and salt water while the sun's up and the weather's warm. Here you can regain some of the perspective on life which has become lost in the general turmoil of living with all its problems and worries. But having got wound down in Druridge Bay, at one with the wilderness, what would you say if some developer was to suddenly charge on to the beach complete with an army of JCB's and tin-hatted draughtsmen and tell you that the area was to be re-scheduled as the site for the country's next twin-reactor nuclear power station?

Your reaction to this shattering of your once-in-a-year bout of tranquillity would probably be unprintable. As you try to collect the fragments of your

Druridge Bay – prime site for the UK's latest nuclear development?

splintered holiday calm, you might even hear the tin-hatted voices of officialdom and progress mumbling about megawatts, megajobs, and megamillions. On the shoreline, meanwhile, your kiddies are silhouetted against the morning sun, paddling at the water's edge, wholly oblivious to the monsters to be created ostensibly for their benefit and future needs. And this is no mere game of make-believe. Druridge Bay is indeed under such a threat, yet the energy needs that the planned power station would fulfil remain unproven.

There's a shortage of clean beaches like Druridge in England. Too many others are either polluted with the many effluents of this sad century or are black with coal slag and the detritus of over 100 years of heavy manufacturing industries. These had their origins in the Industrial Revolution, a stirring period of new inventions, increased production, new jobs and an ever-growing demand for more products. It was then the foundations were laid for many of our problems of today.

The great satanic mills and machine yards, pits, docks and workhouses were the places which helped generate some new wealth. Hundreds of people, men, women and even tiny children slaved away under one roof all the hours that God had given their harsh masters. Why did they bother? To make a living. Because of mechanization, the land no longer provided work for so many. So the people were forced to move from the green despair of the landless labourer to the grey hope of life in industry. It was the age of change, the beginning of the greatest change in the history of our species. We were creating a new environment, constructing things on a scale which would dwarf the pyramids and in quantities never before envisaged.

Workers throughout the world worked away their days and nights to create enormous concentrations of capital, of wealth in the industrial world. Raw materials to fuel the growth were produced thousands of miles away and transported to the great centres of wealth and activity. It was a new kind of work. It was capital-intensive, exhausting, and generating newer and newer supplies of resources and wealth. But it was also labour-intensive. The jobs weren't well paid, but there were lots of them. There were jobs in the textile industry, work in the coal-mines and steel-works, and a host of jobs in the rapidly-developing transport systems.

Times and work were harsh, but in so many ways it was a marvellous era, when the collective human ingenuity of centuries broke new boundaries and was on full display for the whole world to see. But it was also the start of most of the knotty problems of resource over-exploitation, environmental destruction and human relations that we've encountered in our environmental journey. It didn't just produce employment and profit for the British Empire but also swept away many of the crafts and skills of the past, replacing them with hundreds of thousands of mind-blowing, repetitive jobs. And it created pollution the like of which had never ever been dreamt of. It shattered the lives of millions, waged war on the environment, and worst of all it sowed the seeds of future disaster — an all-engrossing attitude towards industrial growth which could never be sustained on a world scale.

The furnaces at Coalbrookdale, UK, home of the Industrial Revolution.

And now it's all gone. The industrial dream of greater and greater production which was going to save mankind lies decaying before us, in the closed factories, empty pits and dole queues. The very goal of higher productivity has meant that people are now displaced by machines. And for most, precious little in the way of satisfying work is being offered in return. The factories of the future don't need lots of workers. They need lots of money to buy lots of machines. The satanic mills of yesterday may have been replaced by environmentally pleasant, modern, airy places alive with the greenery of potted plants and buzzing with activity — but it's not people who are active. Much of the greenery is artificial, like the robot arms of the new electronic work-force and 'brain cells' of the computerized intelligence which operates them. Electronic circuitry might free people from the drudgery of repetitive tasks, but experience shows that it also frees them to join the dole queues.

Computer terminals have taken over where once thousands of office workers went about their jobs. Now a handful of engineers replace components and that's about it. The heavy industries that once dominated our landscapes have been exported to the Third World, together with the long working hours, low pay, bad working conditions and some of the pollution so characteristic of the Victorian sweat-shops. But even worse, the exported industrial bandwagon, the 'waste-drain' also includes many of the 'modern' chemical and nuclear processes which we in the First World would prefer to be without. Something has gone radically wrong. Why is it that, when we have new technologies which could solve our problems all we do is use them to recreate the old ones?

Ultimately the wealth for us all must depend on the resources of the planet. The trouble is even the standard system for *measuring* a country's wealth is utterly mad. GNP – Gross National Product – really is gross, because the value of *all* our goods and services are simply totted up. Pollution, crime, drug abuse – they all cost money and misery. And yet a country which spends a lot on those problems, and they don't add one jot to our real wealth, will actually have a higher GNP than a country which has few of them. The way it is regarded, you would think GNP was a drug, with most politicians firmly hooked on it, crying out for a regular fix.

What is it that the politicians, our elected national and international leaders, are telling us about our future? What do they reckon our children will be doing in the way of jobs? And what sort of environment will our children inherit once their short terms of office are through?

Well there's no getting away from the fact that across Europe the political parties are now talking about the environment, 'green' politics, but in many cases it is just talk, and there's not that much action at the end of the day. It's no good. As soon as they're in office their 'green' ideological growth all too often becomes stunted by a false political spring, infertile immature products of a badly-prepared political seedbed. Loud proclamations of environmental concern are easily made to win a few more votes, yet the real basis of the debates hasn't changed at all. Take a glance through the quickly-assembled green shrubbery at party conference and convention time and you'll see that they're all still planning on the basis of a world of infinite resources. They still reckon it's their duty to use those resources up as quickly as possible. Their vision is so obscured it's clear that the real world passed them by a long time ago and they haven't even bothered to look out and take notice.

If not our leaders, then who does have a clearer view of the real world? Who does have a vision of the earth's future based on sound economic and environmental principles?

One set of groups which claim to have a monopoly of righteousness on visions of the future are the new environmentalists, the Green pressure groups and radical activists, the 'revolutionary front' of the conservation cause. These are a recent phenomena, a spirited, youthful and vigorous offshoot from the roots of traditional conservative conservationism. They first sowed their seeds in the new spring of the 1960s, broke ground in a whole host of organizations in the 1970s, and have emerged in full bloom in the politically barren wastelands of the 1980s. Their growth has been so vigorous, their ideas and passions so plentiful, that the cosiness of traditional conservationism has been stirred from its deep sleep and comforting dreams of butterfly collecting and zoo-keeping. The conservatives have joined ranks with the radicals and it is not uncommon to see lordly peers of the realm, Nobel-prize scientists, English country vicars and the beard-and-sandals brigade all sharing the same political or protest platform. They have a common cause – the environment which we all share – irrespective of their curriculum vitaes. They have a concern for the future of the world, the rightful inheritance of generations to come.

Computer technology at Telecommunications Switching Centre Exchange, Hastings, where human labour becomes superfluous.

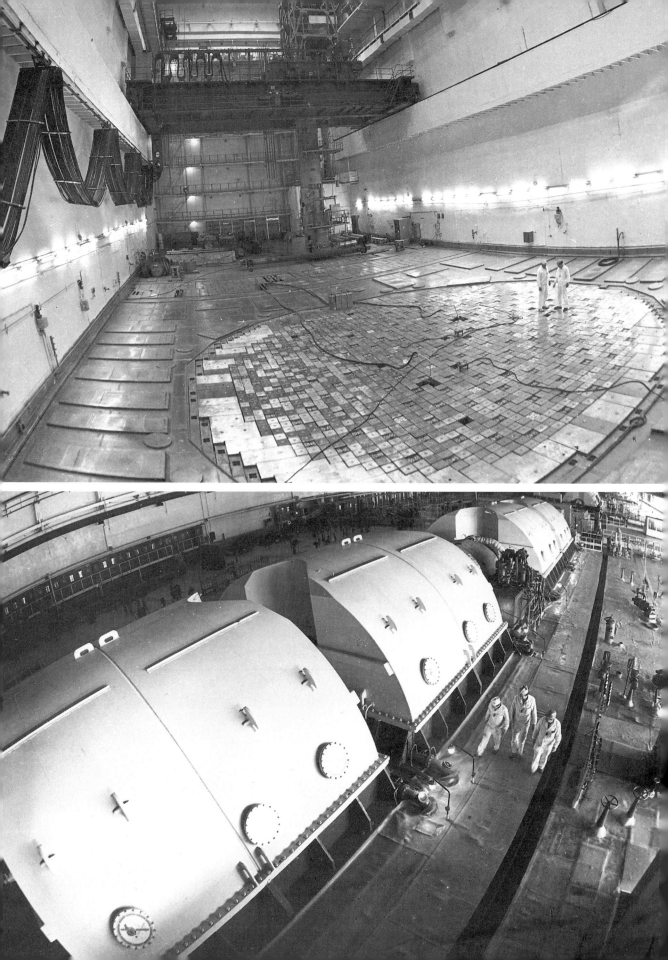

But even more troublesome to some is the effect that the Greens are having on the political map of most western countries. Green-ness is rapidly becoming a measure of political acceptability, and all political parties have their public relations departments operating overtime in trying to put a green camouflage on their grey and highly conservative political colouring. In the UK alone there are thought to be at least 3 million potential environmental votes waiting to be caught at a national election. The numbers are growing constantly, and an estimated fifty parliamentary seats could be won or lost on the strength of attracting support from voters sympathetic to environmental causes, everything from animal rights and countryside conservation, to thwarting plans for development in the green belt and proposals for more nuclear power.

To haul these fertile, passionate catches into a uniformly conservative and somewhat sterile and compromising conventional political net, each of the UK's major political parties produced environmental policy documents for the first time in 1986. These signs of inter-party competition for green credentials are clearly based on opportunism unbridled, but are nevertheless welcome to the true environmentalists. There's been a flowering of new 'green' party spokesmen, some with a considerable personal commitment to the cause, but with limited freedom to act.

Unfortunately, alongside the green growth, there are some depressingly grey shades of political opportunism still lurking. The Greenpeace protest ship *Rainbow Warrior* was sunk in Auckland Sound by an act of international terrorism hatched by senior French Government officials. In the same year, British and French politicians and businessmen launched into planning another initially impressive, but ultimately limited, white elephant scheme – the Channel Tunnel. Like the mega-dams of South America, the Channel Tunnel project is a monument to the illusory belief that large-scale development programmes create long-term employment and prosperity, another case of getting priorities wrong.

In other areas too, the 'brave green words' are seen as little more than a cheap veneer. On the one hand, the international implications and dangers of the disastrous meltdown of the reactor at Chernobyl in the USSR are deplored, on the other, nuclear power programmes continue to proliferate. In the UK alone, new nuclear plant proposals are being shoved into the atom-obsessed electricity generating board's development programme, alongside reprocessing works at Dounreay and Sellafield. There have been proposals for dumping existing stockpiles of radio-active waste in the rural heartlands of southern England. Yet the catalogue of radio-active leaks into the environment from existing nuclear plants is growing at an alarming rate, culminating in 1986, in the Chernobyl disaster which brought home just how destructive and widespread a single accident can be. It's been revealed that the UK's nuclear weapon industry's reactors at Calder Hall and Solway Firth were not constructed to be able to resist even slight earth tremors. The slightest shake in an area where minor tremors are quite common – and each of these reactors, where the core component is suspended above ground-level, could crash to the ground, causing an almighty explosion and a massive radio-active fall-out ... another Chernobyl.

Main hall and turbine house of the reactor room at the Chernobyl atomic power station in the Kiev region ... before the meltdown that shook the world.

With cancerous growths like these lurking in the political undergrowth, it's small wonder that the new green images of politicians from the established parties seem a bit tarnished. More encouraging is the emergence in Europe, of the Green Party (in the UK formerly the Ecology Party). Throughout Europe there are nationally and locally active members all pointing out that 'other parties promise the moon, but only the Green Party guarantees the Earth'. In countries where there is an electoral system of proportional representation, like Germany and Austria, Green politicians are already part of the established political jungle, with elected representatives sitting on local and national democratic assemblies, creating havoc throughout a dark, dusty and worm-eaten jungle of coalitions and electoral pacts. There are green parties or political pressure groups in Australia, France, Belgium, Holland, Austria, Ireland, Sweden, Canada, New Zealand, Japan and the USA, and new groups emerging daily in the Third World – in Malaysia and Indonesia, Africa and Brazil.

But West Germany is the model, with *die Grünen* party having no less than twenty-seven seats in the Bundestag, Germany's national assembly. There's an active membership of 32,000 people, and an estimated 10% of national opinion is behind their long list of radical environmental policies including opposition to the nuclear state and a balanced economy based upon a principle of sustainable growth. In a country where governments are formed out of coalitions, the

David Bellamy, Peter Wilkinson of Greenpeace, and Jonathan Porritt of Friends of the Earth judging the state of the world and its chances for the future.

German Greens have become an attractive alliance spouse in political power-sharing. They are now a serious political force, capable of holding the political as well as the ecological balance, of being a potential arbiter of good government. In Germany, as elsewhere in Europe, the number of local representatives and green voters seem to rise and rise, as environmental problems seem to become more and more insurmountable.

Conventional politicians, feeling threatened by the rapid growth of the Green movement, in all its manifestations, accuse the Greens of impracticality, of excessive idealism, remote from the real world of jobs, human needs and developing technologies. But this can be easily rebutted. There is idealism certainly, but it's a healthy enthusiastic idealism which helps to stretch the boundaries of the possible and challenges a world view of dangerous complacency. The Green dream is fundamentally a progressive and pragmatic vision of the world and of our place in it. In one way, it is ultimate pragmatism, placing the careful management of the earth and its resources, and the servicing of basic human needs, at the very top of an agenda for a better future.

So with the green flag flying on the good ship *Spaceship Earth*, it's time we looked more closely at some of these radical Green ideas. Do the alternatives they put forward really add up to a sane, practical vision of the future, 'rooted', as they say, 'in the earth and not on top of it'? To check out the strength of their Green political convictions, we'll make a theatrical detour — a mock trial of the environmentalists. We provide the judge and counsel; the environmentalists will conduct their own defence, and you, the readers, are the jury.

FUTURE ON TRIAL

CLERK OF COURT: All be upstanding for the case of Green Sanity versus the Status Quo.

JUDGE: I will now hear the evidence of Green Sanity. Will Counsel bring on the first witness please?

COUNSEL: I call upon Mr Jonathan Porrit, a leading international Green and Friend of the Earth.

Now Mr Porrit, could you help us all by explaining exactly what you mean by a sane and sustainable alternative?

JONATHAN PORRIT: For the Green Movement today, sanity means quite simply not killing the goose that lays the golden eggs. The goose in this case is the earth, planet earth. For the simple fact remains that despite all our technological miracles, the earth is the source of all our wealth.

The insanity at the heart of our society today is that we only seem to be creating *our* kind of wealth by destroying the natural wealth of the planet. Now that, literally is not sustainable. If we go on using the earth's non-renewable resources in the way we do now, and abusing the renewable resources such as clean air, water, fertile soil, then the system will simply go bust.

Those who say that the fact it hasn't gone bust yet is proof that it never

Greenpeace's protest ship Rainbow Warrior, before it was destroyed.

will, are dangerous idiots. So far as we're concerned, when we're talking about sustainability, we mean that ecological principles should underlie all economic policy in this country.

COUNSEL: Mr Porrit, at a time when all the major political parties are planning for increased rates of growth, you and the other Green activists are calling for exactly the reverse: a return not to a golden era, but rather to a dark age of environmentally aware, out-of-work wholefood freaks. Not exactly a vote-catcher, is it?

JONATHAN PORRIT: It's true enough that ecology does depend on re-discovering an old wisdom. But that doesn't mean to say we're going to go backwards to discover that wisdom. It means we have to go forwards.

That doesn't mean that we have to accept that the future is nothing more than a continuation of what we have at the present. Because the present simply isn't working. What sane and responsible doctor would actually continue to prescribe medicine to his patients that clearly wasn't working and even worse was seen to be causing additional harm.

Look, it's quite simple in a way. People need good work and there's more than enough of it that needs to be done. The planet needs good, loving, caring management. There are many ways in which we can do that. Now Green economics tells us that those two things aren't contradictory, they go hand-in-hand.

If we could free ourselves of the stranglehold of a centralized, earth-destroying economy and get back to small-scale co-operative production using local resources for local needs, then we both care for the planet and create hundreds of thousands of jobs in the process. The fact is, there isn't the vision around at the moment among all the old-order leaderships to see the ways in which it could all be brought about.

Fishing in the North Sea. Greenpeace believe that if we continue to use the sea as a dumping ground for toxic wastes, there will no longer be any fish harvests to reap.

COUNSEL: Mr Porrit, the kind of change you envisage challenges the very basis of conventional economic thinking. Why on earth should the people who benefit from the system as it now is, give up the power they hold? What political pressures can you bring to bear on them?

JONATHAN PORRIT: I think that pressure will come largely from those people who know the system isn't working for them. It isn't working for the majority of human-kind, particularly in the Third World.

We know that in trampling on the planet the way we do now, we are trampling on the rights of our children and grandchildren. People aren't stupid; they know things have got to change.

It's often slow and superficial, but one has to remember, five years ago people had never heard of the Green Movement, or Green politics. So at a cynical level you might say Green politicians are only in it for the vote. At a deeper level I think we have to acknowledge that the Green Movement represents a significant shift in British society.

And I think at that level it is the primary role of Friends of the Earth and the whole Green Movement, to bring back the sense of vision, and sense of direction that I think has been lacking in world politics for a very long time.

COUNSEL: Yes, I can see the points that you're making, a Green vision eh? That will be all Mr Porrit. Thank you.

For my next witness your honour, I call upon Mr Peter Wilkinson, a leading member of Greenpeace, an international environmental organization with members in many countries of the world.

CLERK OF COURT: Call Mr Wilkinson.

COUNSEL: For the benefit of the court and for those of us who don't see the world through green-tinted glasses, could you please explain what your organization does, and why it does it?

PETER WILKINSON: Greenpeace is an environmental pressure group which tries to bring to the attention of the public the way in which the world is being destroyed. We do this by carrying out what we consider to be peaceful, direct action. This means we physically interfere. We actually get in the way of processes and operations we think are environmentally unsound.

In any campaign we first of all identify our targets. On the whaling issue, where we're trying to protect the last of the great whales, the campaign targets have operations in a number of countries. In the past we've campaigned against Icelandic, Russian, Japanese, and Spanish whaling. We send boats out to sea to get in the way between the whalers and the fleeing whales. Then we physically put our people in front of the whale-catchers, so that when the whale is surfacing at the most vulnerable time, and when the harpoonist is about to strike, our people are in the way forming a human shield. In that way we protect individual whales and obviously give ourselves a very high profile in terms of the media from which to argue our case.

In another campaign which usually takes place in international waters we've tried to prevent the dumping of radio-active waste in the Atlantic by physically putting our vessels underneath the tipping platforms of the ships dumping the waste.

This is a very dangerous protest for us. There's the possibility of a three-ton barrel of lethal waste falling on the dinghy. We're going at thirteen knots because the boat is flat-out trying to avoid the protest. And at the same time we're being hosed down by high-pressure hoses.

Our presence under the dumping ships not only physically prevented some barrels from reaching the ocean bed, but again, gave the issue itself a very high profile from which we successfully argued a thoroughly-researched scientific case that there was no justification at all for dumping radio-active waste in the ocean.

COUNSEL: How can you condone the fact that people like yourselves disrupt, in what must be considered an illegal manner, perfectly legal and viable commercial activities?

PETER WILKINSON: Well the fact of the matter is that we believe that the environment does not belong exclusively to the UK Atomic Energy Author-

The Greenpeace protest vessel Rainbow Warrior in Auckland Harbour after two explosions ripped through it.

ity or to the Japanese Whaling Association or to any particular minority of governments or industries. It's part of our common heritage. It belongs to all of us.

If we don't act soon, that common heritage will no longer be worth inheriting. It's in immediate danger. Just look at a few examples of what could happen if we don't act quickly and purposefully now.

Within the next ten years the North Sea will become biologically dead because we are continuing to use it as a rubbish tip for our toxic waste. In the next twenty years a third of the arable land that we currently use will become unusable because of the way we're misusing the soil. In the next eighty-five years, if we carry on chopping down the rain forests at the rate we are at the moment, we won't have any rain forests left at all.

And by the end of the century, it's expected that if we continue to export nuclear power technology, over forty countries, many of them very unstable, will have nuclear weapons capability: their own stock-pile of plutonium bombs.

It all adds up to a total environmental and human tragedy performed largely without the consent of the world's living and voting audiences, and that includes *you*, honourable members of the jury. And if the show is allowed to continue until the very last act, the stage and the audience will be totally obliterated and there will be no-one left around to mourn their passing.

JUDGE: We'll have no direct action in this courtroom. Could the witness please address his remarks only to the Counsel.

PETER WILKINSON: Well your honour, we in Greenpeace are not prepared to sit back and watch the piece-meal destruction of the planet by environmental degradation or the potential wholesale destruction of the planet by the unthinkable nightmare of a nuclear holocaust. It's our planet and we want to protect it. And we will physically but peacefully do so.

COUNSEL: Thank you Mr Wilkinson. With the permission of the court, I'd like you to confirm or deny whether your actions and activities you describe are indeed advanced in support of measures which are wholly justifiable on scientific as well as moral grounds.

PETER WILKINSON: Indeed. In two of our major recent campaigns against the nuclear industry, for the closing of the Sellafield Nuclear Fuel Reprocessing Plant and against the dumping of radio-active waste in the sea, we commissioned scientific reports by independent consultants on the safety hazards of both types of operation. In both cases the consultants reinforced our view that these processes and procedures were morally and environmentally outrageous.

Responsible objective scientific research conducted unusually in this field by bodies without a vested interest or organizational link to the bodies responsible for Sellafield and nuclear dumping, has come down firmly on our side.

COUNSEL: In its time Greenpeace has made some very powerful and bitter enemies

*Benares, India – A prayer for
the rising run ... and the future
of the world?*

who see you as threatening their interests, their survival, their futures.
Some of your enemies include democratically-elected governments, who
claim to represent the views and wishes of their people. Doesn't the backlash
put you off? Didn't the sinking of your boat, the *Rainbow Warrior*, represent
the sinking of your cause – an indication that this time your non-violent
action had gone just too far, threatening the integrity and strategic survival
of a nation itself? Did not the Rainbow Dream go down with the sinking of
your ship?

PETER WILKINSON: Definitely not. I think those people that bombed the *Rainbow
Warrior* in nuclear-free New Zealand are now ruing the day they did it.
What they've effectively done is given us a much higher profile than ever
before. I think everybody throughout the world now knows what the French
are doing in the Pacific, unnecessarily testing nuclear weapons.

I believe that their actions are an example of the way in which Greenpeace
is touching a raw nerve among some governments and some industries. But
it's also a testament of the effectiveness of the organization. In the Pacific
Ocean now there is occurring a general unification of all the desperate voices
of protest. The people of those beleaguered islands want to see their ocean,

their environment, being used no longer as a nuclear laboratory for the super powers, a playground for their nuclear obsessions. For their defence they turned to Greenpeace, because no-one else would help. I think though that their voices are now being heard. Ultimately we will win because we are bringing the attention of the world to some disgraceful goings on, we are influencing world opinion.

COUNSEL: Thank you Mr Wilkinson for explaining to us how you see the Green Vision converted into reality through environmental action. But are the Greens winning? Is the action working? Is the message of Green Sanity really getting across? Is it getting through, for example, to the current upholders of the status-quo, the leaders of our current political parties? To answer that I'd like to call one final witness, Petra Kelly, a prominent waver of the international green flag, and a democratically-elected member of the West German parliament, the Bundestag.

CLERK OF THE COURT: Call the final witness, Petra Kelly.

COUNSEL: Could you tell the court whether you think the new 'greening' of the major political parties shows this time colours? And does it go far enough?

PETRA KELLY: Well, if you look at the development of other parties they do try to colour themselves cosmetically green, they try to make up that they're green, but they still don't look at the sources of the problems. In the issue of stopping acid rain, in the issue of making lead-free gasoline, we've always noticed that the issues are becoming popular, are becoming fashionable, but people do not often look at what is at the true source of the damage. And that is, I think, the message of the Green, always trying to name the true sources and not being subtle about it.

COUNSEL: You seem to have a different view of politics from the other political parties. You call ecology, your Green politics, a 'politics for life'. What does this mean?

PETRA KELLY: I think ecology must be understood not as a part of politics, it is politics. It means a respect for living things, it means respect for, and being a lobby for, plants, for animals, for eco-systems. It means also the earth has no emergency exit. We must manage to live together ecologically, sustainably, or we'll exploit each other to death ... blow each other up.

The central message of the Green movement, as I see it is the interconnectedness of policies, of work, energy, food, and defence, our natural resources and our life-styles, and the balance which must be maintained within and between these things. It's a balance that proceeds from the laws of nature itself, and especially from the knowledge that unlimited growth is impossible in a limited system. We are part of a limited eco-system which the policies and politics of the old order is threatening to destroy. An enlightened green view means looking at our environment and at the planet earth as one unit, one international living unit. We are all together within this unit, inter-connected. We have to begin to make life an ecological balance or else we'll die.

COUNSEL: Thank you Petra Kelly and the other witnesses for demonstrating and defending the Green case. Counsel rests.

THE JUDGE: Thank you Counsel. I have listened carefully to everything that has been said. But before the court adjourns to consider the evidence now placed before us, I think it would be helpful if I were to list the cardinal principles on which this case should be judged. These are the three new commandments, upon which all our futures will be decided (reads from scroll): which could guarantee the survival of the species and the environment in which we live:

First we must look after the living world, the seas, soils, lakes, rivers and landsdapes on which we all depend, these are our only life support systems.

Second we must stop wasting our non-renewable resources, and that includes the genetic reservoirs of all the world's plants and animals.

Third we must learn to re-cycle, and to develop our renewable resources to provide for a planned population of well-fed, well-educated sharing people.

CLERK OF COURT: The case of Green Sanity against the Status Quo has now been heard, the Court and the Jury will now adjourn to consider their verdict. Will all be upstanding.

THE FINAL JUDGEMENT

The trial over, we're now at the end of our journey, and we rest our case and our labours on that beach at the turning of the tide.

Well, what was your verdict? You have participated in our journey across the life-support systems of *Spaceship Earth*. You've seen the damage done, heard the case of the Greens, and witnessed some of the options which lie before us, options which we believe secure the survival of our species and guarantee future life on earth.

But whatever your views and sympathies, whatever your perspective, be it local or global, any final judgement and any action which arises from it, must involve a recognition of the need to restore the balance between development and the environment, between culture and nature, between humanity and the natural world. It must mean putting in order the imbalances in the use of our resources, the imbalance between First and Third Worlds, and the imbalance in our own lives which leads us both to pollute our world and destroy that which cannot be replaced.

It is clear to us that we cannot carry on as we have done. To do that would be to embrace our own extinction. We have to take further the alternatives, old and new, which do exist. And in the true spirit of scientific endeavour, we have to explore new options, new ways of doing things, new ways of meeting the needs of all. But this time, and with the wisdom of experience, these new ways have to be sustainable, they must not harm the earth or drive us to the brink.

Realizing the fragility of our world and understanding the true nature of the dangers we have created for ourselves are important steps in creating positive change and providing hope for the future. But whatever new routes we follow, whatever decisions we make, whatever actions we take, the forward passage of *Spaceship Earth* hangs in the balance.

Overleaf
Back to the beginning: our case, our future rests with turning the tide of destruction into a tide of hope that cleanses and renews.

Change is in the air, the tide is turning. On the beach a new day is approaching. There's a full moon over the land, fading in the brightening sky. The new tide, rolling in on the shoreline, brings with it a myriad of new beginnings, waves of new hope and new life.

The sun is just about to rise above the horizon. And there's a drop of sweet early morning rain. In the distance, a soft green light glows. And a rainbow arches up across the sky, over the sea and over the land.

INDEX

QUOTATION SOURCES

1. *Touch the Earth*, T. C. McLuhan, Abacus, 1973; 2. *I Have Spoken*, V. I. Armstrong, Swallow Press, 1971; 3. *Touch the Earth*, T. C. McLuhan, Abacus, 1973; 4. From *The Social & Environmental Effects of Large Dams*, E. Goldsmith & N. Hildyard, Ecoropa, 1984; 5. Presidential Address to the Ramblers' Association, P. Melchett, 1984; 6. *The Quest for Gaia*, Dr James Lovelock, *New Scientist*, 1975; 7. *No Immediate Danger*, Rosalie Bertell, The Women's Press, 1985; 8. Quoted in *Agriculture, the Countryside and Land Use*, J. K. Bowers & Paul Cheshire, Methuen, 1983; 9. From *The Forest Connection*, Prof. L. Roche, Gorta, 1985; 10. *Farming in the Clouds*, Richard Body, Temple Smith, 1984; 11. William Beebe, quoted in *A Wealth of Wild Species*, Norman Myers, Westview, 1983; 12. Publicity brochure, Itaipu Binacional, Brazil; 13. *The Social and Environmental Effects of Large Dams*, E. Goldsmith & N. Hildyard, Ecoropa, 1984; 14. *The Franklin: Not Just a River*, James McQueen, Penguin, 1983; 15. *Population, Resources, Environment*, Paul R. Ehrlich & Anne H. Ehrlich, Freeman, 1970; 16. Roger E. Batzel: written submission to Armed Services Committee, US House of Representatives, 1985; 17. *Towards 2000*, Raymond Williams, Cape, 1983; 18. *Nuclear Winter*, O. Greene, I. Percival, I. Ridge, Blackwell, 1985; 19. *Towards 2000*, Raymond Williams, Cape, 1983; 20. *The Fate of the Earth*, Jonathan Schell, Cape, 1982.

REFERENCES

Common Crisis: North/South: Co-operation for World Recovery, Brandt Commission, Pan, 1983

The Conservation and Development Programme for the UK; A Response to the World Conservation Strategy, The Programme Organizing Committee, Kogan Page, 1983

The Environmental Crisis, ed. Des Wilson, Heinemann, 1984

The Gaia Atlas of Planet Management, ed. Norman Myers, Pan, 1985

Gaia: A New Look at Life on Earth, James Lovelock, OUP, 1979

Global 2000 Report to the President, Penguin, 1982

Nuclear Power, Walter Patterson, Penguin, 1983

The Primary Source, Norman Myers

Seeing Green, Jonathan Porritt, Blackwell, 1984

The State of the Environment, 1985, OECD, 1985

The Turning Point, Fritjof Capra, Flamingo/Fontana, 1982

A Wealth of Wild Species, Norman Myers, Westview, 1983

Whose Land is it Anyway? Richard Norton Taylor, Turnstone Press, 1982

Working the Land, Charlie Pye-Smith & Richard North, Temple Smith, 1984

World Conservation Strategy: An Overview – Resourceful Britain? Brian Johnson, Kogan Page, 1983

ILLUSTRATIONS CREDITS

p. 10 *Allan Power, Bruce Coleman Ltd*; 2 *NASA, Bruce Coleman Ltd*; 26–7 *Tony Stone*; 14 top *D. Henderson*; 14 bottom *Mark Edwards, Earthscan*; 18–19 *Ivor Edmonds*; 16 *Brendan Quayle*; 24 *US Task Force One, Associated Press*; 30 *D. Williams*; 42 *Edward S. Curtis*; 20 *Frans Lanting, Bruce Coleman Ltd*; 21 *International Development Action*; 34 *Tony Stone*; 35 *Bewick woodcut*; 38–9 *D. Williams*; 46 *Brendan Quayle*; 47 *Brendan Quayle*; 50–1 *Rik Walton*; 55 *NASA (taken from Skylab), Bruce Coleman Ltd*; 58 *Brendan Quayle*; 73 *Tony Stone*; 76 top *Tony Stone*; 68 *British Nuclear Fuels*; 63 *Francisco Erize, Bruce Coleman Ltd*; 62 *Mary Evans Picture Library*; 81 *D. Henderson*; 77 *Leroy F. Grannis, Planet Earth Pictures*; 76 bottom *Ace Photo Agency*; 83 *Mary Evans Picture Library*; 80 *Ace Photo Agency*; 90 *Bewick woodcut*; 92 *Nicholas Devore, Bruce Coleman Ltd*; 93 *David Hosking*; 91 *Bewick woodcut*; 88 *D. Henderson*; 89 *Chris Prior, Planet Earth Pictures*; 100 *Murray Watson, Biofotos*; 101 *P. Davey, Frank Lane Picture Agency*; 96 *Shell Photographic Library*; 104 *D. Henderson*; 108 *Brendan Quayle*; 109 *Brendan Quayle*; 113 *Brendan Quayle*; 114 *Brendan Quayle*; 120 *Alan Walmsley*; 124 *Dave Williams*; 125 top left *John Markham, Bruce Coleman Ltd* (Kingfisher); 125 top right *Hans Rheinland, Bruce Coleman Ltd*; *D. Henderson*; 121 *Eric Crichton, Bruce Coleman Ltd*; 125 bottom *Heather Angel*; 128 *Northumbria Air Fotos*; 130 *A. Dobrauska, Ace Photo Agency*; 131 *David Hosking*; 134 *Heather Angel*; 136 *Greenpeace*; 139 *Nicholas Devore, Bruce Coleman Ltd*; 146 *Frank Lane Picture Agency*; 158 top *Soames Summerhays, Biofotos*; 149 *Mary Evans Picture Agency*; 147 *Frank Lane Picture Agency*; 155 *Adrian Davies, Bruce Coleman Ltd*; 150 *Mark Edwards, Earthscan*; 157 *Mary Evans Picture Library*; 158 bottom *Roy Deane*; 154 *David Williams*; 161 *Mary Evans Picture Library*; 166 *Brendan Quayle*; 167 *Brendan Quayle*; 164 *Mary Evans Picture Library*; 171 *Tony Stone*; 174 *Dieter and Mary Plage, Bruce Coleman Ltd*; 175 *Tony Stone*; 177 *Northumbrian Water*; 181 *G. W. Frame, Bruce Coleman Ltd*; 182 *International Development Action*; 184 *Mark N. Boulton, Bruce Coleman Ltd*; 185 *Heather Angel*; 187 *Fay Godwin's Photo Files*; 189 *Daily Telegraph Colour Library*; 193 *Mark Edwards, Earthscan*; 193 *Ron Cartmell, Bruce Coleman Ltd*; 195 *Oxfam*; 197 *Heather Angel*; 201 top *Brendan Quayle*; 201 bottom *D. Henderson*; 200 *Mary Evans Picture Library*; 204–5 *Patrick Eager*; 208 *Christian Zuber, Bruce Coleman Ltd*; 214 *Associated Press*; 209 *Bruce Coleman Ltd*; 212 *Daily Telegraph Colour Library*; 222 *Fotochronika, TASS*; 217 *Brendan Quayle*; 219 *Mary Evans Picture Library*; 220 *Tony Stone*; 224 *Brendan Quayle*; 229 *Associated Press*; 227 *Photo Library International*; 226 *Greenpeace*; 231 *D. Henderson*; 234–5 *Photo Library International*; Back jacket *David Williams*.